Help yourself to
differentiation

Hugh Neill

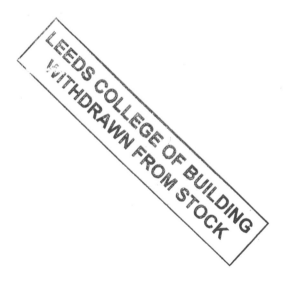
 LONGMAN

Pearson Education Limited
Edinburgh Gate
Harlow
Essex
CM20 2JE
England and Associated Companies throughout the World

First published 1997
Second impression 2000
Printed in Singapore (KHL)

ISBN 0582 31796 7

Contents

Preface

The purpose of this book is to help to increase students' facility in the early parts of the differential calculus.

There are plenty of exercises in this book. The exercises are graded, and most types of exercise have a worked example with a full commentary to provide assistance.

I would like to thank the authors of New General Mathematics, Messrs J B Channon, A McLeish Smith and H C Head, for allowing me to use their text for the sections on maxima and minima and for curve sketching, Rosemary Emanuel for checking the manuscripts and her many helpful suggestions, Sue Maunder for checking the answers and Addison Wesley Longman for their speed in producing this book.

The responsibility for any errors is mine.

Hugh Neill
March 7, 1997

1 How to use this book

Assumptions made

This is a book which is designed to help you to learn differential calculus by giving you a number of carefully worked examples, and then problems based on them.

The assumption is that you are not a beginner, and that you have been taught some calculus already. Thus, no theory is given; if you need to know more, then you should consult your calculus book and your teacher.

At the beginning of each chapter there is a list of topics which you should have studied and understood before commencing work.

Most of the techniques are introduced in the context of polynomials. Chapters 13 and 14 introduce the trigonometric, exponential and logarithmic functions. There follow three short chapters on implicit differentiation, parametric differentiation, small increases and curve sketching.

Learning a technique

Suppose that you need to learn how to carry out a particular technique. Look for the chapter which includes the technique, check that you have covered the theory, and then study the worked examples carefully, preferably with a pen in your hand.

Write down the steps as you go, and check each step carefully. Ask yourself: Why was this particular step chosen? Do I agree with the working? Why is it like that?

Remember that mathematics is not disconnected, and if you can learn the general principles behind calculus, you will make better progress in other areas of the subject.

Trying the exercises

If you get stuck with a particular exercise, then look back at a worked example similar to the one you are having difficulty with, and try to isolate the place where you are having the problem.

Look at the answer. Sometimes, but not always, the general form of the answer can give you a clue. Remember that sometimes there can be different forms of the same answer, and it may be that your answer is correct, but you do not recognise it as such.

There are plenty of exercises in the book. Do as many as you need to perfect a technique.

Short cuts

In many cases the examples are worked in more detail than you need to give in a solution. If you can skip lines, go ahead; but don't make errors by so doing! It is better to write more steps, and to get the solution correct, than to skip steps, get things wrong, and subsequently lose confidence.

Graphics calculators

No mention is made of graphics calculators in this book. If you have one available, you should certainly use it where appropriate. However, problems in calculus need exact techniques, which are the focus of this book.

Other non-calculus methods

This is a book about differential calculus, so it follows that calculus methods are given for solving the problems in this book. However, there are other occasions when a non-calculus method may be quicker, for example, in certain maximum and minimum problems, and in curve sketching.

Answers

Answers are given, but in some cases the answer given may be in a form different from yours. If that is so, and you cannot reconcile your answer with that in the book, you should seek help.

2 Gradient curves

You will need to know

● how to find the gradient of a straight line given two points on it

● the difference between a line with positive gradient and a line with negative gradient, shown in Fig. 2.1.

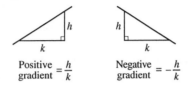

Positive gradient $= \dfrac{h}{k}$ Negative gradient $= -\dfrac{h}{k}$

Fig. 2.1

If you are given a graph, you can measure or estimate the gradient at each value of x. You can then plot the values of the gradient against the value of x to get another graph. It is useful to be able to deduce the approximate shape of the gradient graph from the graph of the original function.

1 For which parts of the graph in Fig. 2.2 is the gradient positive and for which parts is the gradient negative?

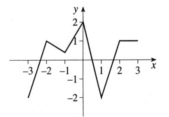

Fig. 2.2

| Gradient is positive when a graph slopes upwards and to the right, negative for downwards to the right, and zero when horizontal. | The intervals for positive gradient are: $-3 < x < -2$, $-1 < x < 0$ and $1 < x < 2$. |

| At the sharp joins of the straight lines the gradient does not exist. | The intervals for negative gradient are: $-2 < x < -1$ and $0 < x < 1$. |

2 For which part of the graph in Fig. 2.2 is the gradient greatest and for which part is the gradient least?

| Look at the numerical values of the gradient in the pieces. | The greatest gradient is 3 in the intervals $-3 < x < -2$ and $1 < x < 2$. |
| Look for the greatest and the smallest numerical values of the gradient. | The least gradient is -4 in the interval $0 < x < 1$. |

3 In question **1**, you are told that the gradients are 3, -0.5, 1.5, -4, 3 and 0. Draw a graph of the gradient against x.

| Draw the values of the gradient for the intervals of the graph in Fig. 2.2.

Notice that there are breaks in the gradient graph corresponding to the sharp points of the joins in Fig. 2.2.

Note that when the graph in Fig. 2.2 is steepest, the corresponding parts of the gradient graph are furthest away from the x-axis. | 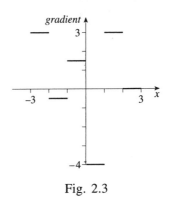
Fig. 2.3 |

When the original graph is curved, drawing the gradient graph is more approximate, and you can probably only give a very rough sketch which shows its general shape.

4 For the part of the graph shown in Fig. 2.4, where is the gradient zero? Where is the gradient greatest and least?

| The gradient is zero when the graph is horizontal. | The gradient is zero at $x = -1$. |

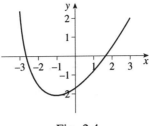

Fig. 2.4

| The graph has greatest gradient when it is steepest to the right, and least when it is sloping downwards to the right. | The greatest gradient is at $x = 3$ and the least gradient is at $x = -3$. |

5 Sketch the graph of the gradient for the graph in Fig. 2.5.

The gradient is 0 at $x = -1$, so plot the point $(-1, 0)$ on the gradient graph.

On the left of $x = -1$, that is, for $-3 < x < -1$, the gradient is negative, so the graph of the gradient is negative and below the x-axis.

Similarly, the gradient is positive for $-1 < x < 3$ so the graph of the gradient is positive and above the x-axis.

The exact shape is vague, so the graduations have been removed from the graph of the gradient against x.

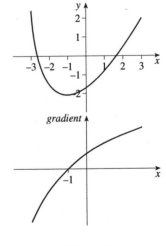

Fig. 2.5

6 Sketch the graph of the gradient against x for the graph shown in Fig. 2.6.

Here is an outline of the method.

● Determine first the points of the original graph at which the gradient is zero, and mark the appropriate points on the x-axis of the gradient graph.

5

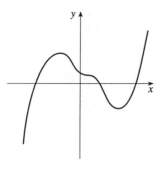

Fig. 2.6

● Between the points of zero gradient, mark the curve with positive and negative signs corresponding to the gradient as shown in the top part of Fig. 2.7. If the gradient is positive, the sign will be positive; if the gradient is large, the positive sign will also be large.

● Then use the information gained to plot the gradient graph, shown in the lower part of Fig. 2.7.

The points marked 0 on the graph refer to the points of zero gradient. These points give rise to points on the *x*-axis on the gradient graph.

Then the parts of the curve with positive gradient are marked with + signs; the larger the + sign, the larger the gradient. These points give rise to points on the gradient graph *above* the *x*-axis, since the gradient is positive.

The parts with negative gradient give rise to points below the *x*-axis on the gradient graph.

The points are then joined up to form a sketch of the gradient graph.

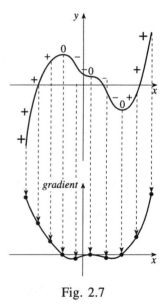

Fig. 2.7

Exercise 2

1 For the graph in Fig. 2.8, write down the maximum and the minimum gradients, and draw the graph of the gradient.

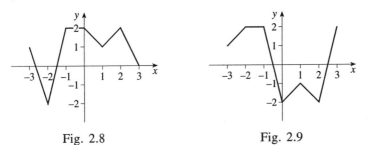

Fig. 2.8   Fig. 2.9

2 For the graph in Fig. 2.9, write down the maximum and the minimum gradients, and draw the gradient graph.

3 For the graph in Fig. 2.10, write down the intervals of x for which the gradient is positive, and those for which the gradient is negative. Sketch its gradient graph, making it clear where the gradient graph crosses the x-axis.

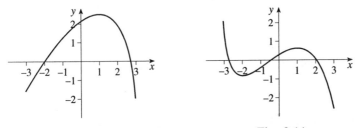

Fig. 2.10   Fig. 2.11

4 For the graph in Fig. 2.11, write down the intervals of x for which the gradient is positive, and those for which the gradient is negative. Sketch its gradient graph, making it clear where the gradient graph crosses the x-axis.

3   Differentiating powers of x

You will need to know

- that the derivative of x^n is nx^{n-1} for all values of n

- how to differentiate sums, differences and multiples of powers of x

- that the words 'differentiate' and 'find the derived function', 'find $\dfrac{dy}{dx}$', 'find the gradient function' and 'find $f'(x)$' all have the same meaning

- the meaning of, and how to manipulate, indices

- how to find the equation of a line through a given point with a given gradient.

You will find that, just as there is alternative language for the process of differentiation, there is also alternative notation. In the examples which follow, you will see alternative forms of language and notation.

1   Find $\dfrac{dy}{dx}$ when $y = x^3$, $y = 2x^4$, $y = 2x + 3$ and $y = 5x^3 - 4x^2 + 2$.

Use the nx^{n-1} rule.	If $y = x^3$, $\dfrac{dy}{dx} = 3x^2$.
Constant multiples do not affect the nx^{n-1} rule. It is not usual to write this out in the detail given.	If $y = 2 \times x^4$, then $\dfrac{dy}{dx} = 2 \times 4x^3 = 8x^3$.
Sums of functions are differentiated term by term. Note that $y = 2x + 3$ is the equation of a straight line with gradient 2.	If $y = 2x + 3$, $\dfrac{dy}{dx} = 2$.
Sums of functions are differentiated term by term. Use the nx^{n-1} rule on each term separately.	If $y = 5x^3 - 4x^2 + 2$, then $\dfrac{dy}{dx} = 15x^2 - 8x$.

8

2 Find $f'(x)$ for each of the following functions $f(x)$.
$f(x) = x^{-1}$, $f(x) = x^{\frac{1}{2}}$, $f(x) = x^0$ and $f(x) = x^2 - 2x^{-1}$.

The nx^{n-1} rule still works. Leave the answer in the same form as it was given.	If $f(x) = x^{-1}$, then $f'(x) = -1 \times x^{-2} = -x^{-2}$.
Use the nx^{n-1} rule again. Leave the answer in the same form as it was given.	If $f(x) = x^{\frac{1}{2}}$, then $f'(x) = \frac{1}{2}x^{-\frac{1}{2}}$.
Use the nx^{n-1} rule. You should recognise that $x^0 = 1$, so you are being asked to differentiate a constant and get 0.	If $f(x) = x^0$, then $f'(x) = 0 \times x^{-1} = 0$.
Differentiate term by term. Once again, leave the answer in the form in which the question was asked.	If $f(x) = x^2 - 2x^{-1}$, then $f'(x) = 2x - 2 \times x^{-2} \times (-1)$ $= 2x + 2x^{-2}$.

3 Find the derived functions of $f(x) = \dfrac{1}{x}$, $f(x) = \sqrt{x}$ and $f(x) = \dfrac{-2}{\sqrt{x}}$.

Express $\dfrac{1}{x}$ as a power of x to differentiate it. Then return it to the positive power form in which the function was given.	$f(x) = \dfrac{1}{x} = x^{-1}$ $f'(x) = -1 \times x^{-2}$ $= -1 \times \dfrac{1}{x^2} = -\dfrac{1}{x^2}$.
You must express $\sqrt{x}$ as a power of x to differentiate it. Then return it to its original form using the standard index rules.	$f(x) = \sqrt{x} = x^{\frac{1}{2}}$ $f'(x) = \frac{1}{2}x^{-\frac{1}{2}}$ $= \frac{1}{2} \times \dfrac{1}{\sqrt{x}} = \dfrac{1}{2\sqrt{x}}$.

9

Express $\dfrac{-2}{\sqrt{x}}$ in power form, and then differentiate. In this case it is usual to give the answer as a positive power rather than $-\dfrac{1}{\sqrt{x^3}}$.

$f(x) = \dfrac{-2}{\sqrt{x}} = -2x^{-\frac{1}{2}}$

$f'(x) = -2 \times \left(-\tfrac{1}{2}\right)x^{-\frac{3}{2}}$

$= \dfrac{1}{x^{\frac{3}{2}}}$ or simply $x^{-\frac{3}{2}}$.

Here are some other examples where you need to manipulate the form of the expression before differentiating. The objective is to get the expression as the sum of powers of x, and then you can apply the nx^{n-1} rule for differentiation.

4   Find the differential coefficients of $(2x+1)^2$, $\dfrac{x^2+1}{x}$, $\sqrt{(2x)}$, $\dfrac{2}{\sqrt{3x}}$.

This is not in the form of a sum of powers of x, but you can make it so by first multiplying out the brackets.

Let $y = (2x+1)^2$.
Then $y = 4x^2 + 4x + 1$, so
$\dfrac{dy}{dx} = 8x + 4$.

You can express this as a sum of powers by first dividing.

Let $y = \dfrac{x^2+1}{x} = x + \dfrac{1}{x} = x + x^{-1}$.
Then $\dfrac{dy}{dx} = 1 - x^{-2} = 1 + \dfrac{1}{x^2}$.

To differentiate this function separate it into the form $\sqrt{(2x)} = \sqrt{2} \times \sqrt{x}$.

Let $y = \sqrt{(2x)} = \sqrt{2} \times \sqrt{x}$
$= \sqrt{2} \times x^{\frac{1}{2}}$.
Then $\dfrac{dy}{dx} = \sqrt{2} \times \dfrac{1}{2} \times x^{-\frac{1}{2}} = \dfrac{\sqrt{2}}{2\sqrt{x}}$.

To differentiate this function separate it into the form $\dfrac{2}{\sqrt{3x}} = \dfrac{2}{\sqrt{3}} \times \dfrac{1}{\sqrt{x}}$.

Let $y = \dfrac{2}{\sqrt{3x}} = \dfrac{2}{\sqrt{3}} \times \dfrac{1}{\sqrt{x}} = \dfrac{2}{\sqrt{3}} x^{-\frac{1}{2}}$.
Then $\dfrac{dy}{dx} = \dfrac{2}{\sqrt{3}} \times -\dfrac{1}{2} x^{-\frac{3}{2}} = -\dfrac{1}{\sqrt{3}} x^{-\frac{3}{2}}$.

The derivative gives you useful information about the gradient of the curve whose equation you are differentiating. The examples which follow show you different ways in which you can use the derivative.

5 Find the gradient of the graph $y = x^2 + 3x - 1$ at the points on it where $x = 3$ and $x = -2$.

First differentiate to find the gradient at any point.	$y = x^2 + 3x - 1$ $\dfrac{dy}{dx} = 2x + 3.$
Then put x equal to the values required.	When $x = 3$, gradient $= 2 \times 3 + 3 = 9$. When $x = -2$, gradient $= 2 \times (-2) + 3 = -1$.

6 Find the points on the graph $y = x^3 + 3x^2 - 9x + 3$ at which the gradient is 15.

First differentiate to find the gradient at any point.	$y = x^3 + 3x^2 - 9x + 3$ $\dfrac{dy}{dx} = 3x^2 + 6x - 9.$
To find when the gradient is 15, put $\dfrac{dy}{dx} = 15$, and then solve the resulting quadratic equation by any of the usual methods, factorising or using the quadratic equation formula.	Gradient $= 15$ when $\dfrac{dy}{dx} = 15$ so $3x^2 + 6x - 9 = 15$. Solving: $3x^2 + 6x - 24 = 0$ $x^2 + 2x - 8 = 0$ $(x + 4)(x - 2) = 0$ $x = -4$ or $x = 2$.

To find the required points you need the values of the y-coordinates as well as the x-coordinates. So substitute into the equation $y = x^3 + 3x^2 - 9x + 3$ to find y.	When $x = 2$, $y = 2^3 + 3 \times 2^2 - 9 \times 2 + 3$ $= 8 + 12 - 18 + 3 = 5$. Similarly, when $x = -4$, $y = 23$.
Finally, give the coordinates of the points.	The required points are $(2, 5)$ and $(-4, 23)$.

Exercise 3

Find $\dfrac{dy}{dx}$ for each of the following functions y. Where they appear, a, b and c are constants.

1   $7x^2$ 2 $5x^3$

3   ax 4 bx^2

5   cx^3 6 $x^2 + 4x + 1$

7   $3x^2 - 5x$ 8 $x^3 + x^2$

9   x^4 10 $6x^4$

11   $2x^3 - 3x^2$ 12 x^5

13   $3x^2 - 7x - 4$ 14 $4 + 6x - 7x^2$

15   $x^3 - 5x^2 + 3x - 2$ 16 $2x^3 - 4x^2 + x + 1$

Find the derivatives with respect to x of the following functions.

17   x^{-2} 18 $2x^{-1}$

19   $-2x^{-3} + \frac{1}{2}x^{-2}$ 20 $\frac{1}{3}x^{-3} + \frac{1}{2}x^2$

21   $2x^0$ 22 $8x + 4x^{-2}$

23   $3x - 3x^{-3}$ 24 $2x^{\frac{1}{2}}$

25   $3x^{-\frac{2}{3}}$ 26 $3x^{\frac{1}{3}} + 2x^{-2} + x$

27   $1 + 2x - 2x^{-3}$ 28 $4x^{\frac{3}{2}} - 2x^{-\frac{1}{2}} + 3x - 2$

Differentiate each of the following functions.

29   $\dfrac{1}{x^2}$ 30 $2\sqrt{x} - 3x$

31 $\dfrac{1}{\sqrt{x}}$ **32** $\sqrt{x^3}$

33 $(x+3)^2$ **34** $(2x+1)(2x-1)$

35 $\left(x+\dfrac{1}{x}\right)^2$ **36** $\left(\sqrt{x}+\dfrac{1}{\sqrt{x}}\right)^2$

37 $\dfrac{x+1}{x}$ **38** $\left(\dfrac{x+1}{x}\right)^2$

39 $(x-1)(x^2+x+1)$ **40** $\dfrac{(x+1)(x^2-x+1)}{x}$

41 $(2x)^2$ **42** $(3x)^{\frac{1}{2}}$

43 $\sqrt{(4x)}$ **44** $\sqrt[3]{(3x)}$

Find the y-coordinate, and the gradient, at the points on the following curves corresponding to the given values of x.

45 $y = x^2 + 3x + 2$, $x = 1$ **46** $y = 2x^2 + x - 1$, $x = 2$

47 $y = 2x - x^2$, $x = 0$ **48** $y = x(x-1)$, $x = -2$

49 $y = x(x-1)(x-2)$, $x = 3$ **50** $y = \sqrt{x}$, $x = 4$

For each of the following curves, find the point or points at which the gradient has the given value.

51 $y = 2x^2$, gradient 4   **52** $y = 3x^2 + 2x$, gradient -4

53 $y = \dfrac{1}{x}$, gradient -4 **54** $y = x^{\frac{3}{2}}$, gradient 6

55 $y = x^3 - 3x^2 + 5x - 6$, gradient 2

56 $y = x^3 - 2x^2 + x - 3$, gradient 5

4   Tangents and normals

You will need to know

- how to find the equation of a straight line given its gradient and a point which lies on it
- how to find the gradient of a line perpendicular to a given line
- the meaning of the word 'normal', shown in Fig. 4.1.

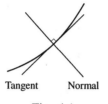

Tangent   Normal

Fig. 4.1

You can use differentiation to find the equation of the tangent to a curve through a given point.

1   Find the equation of the tangent at $(2,4)$ to the graph of $y = x^2$.

You can find the equation of a straight line if you know its gradient and the coordinates of a point on it. As you know $(2,4)$ lies on the line, you only need its gradient. To find the gradient, differentiate the equation $y = x^2$ of the curve.

Differentiate to find the gradient.	If $y = x^2$, $\dfrac{dy}{dx} = 2x$.
For the gradient at $x = 2$, substitute $x = 2$ in the expression for $\dfrac{dy}{dx}$.	When $x = 2$, $\dfrac{dy}{dx} = 4$, so the gradient is 4.

Use $y - Y = m(x - X)$ to find the equation of the line through (X, Y) with gradient m.	The tangent has gradient 4 and passes through $(2, 4)$, so its equation is $y - 4 = 4(x - 2)$.
Then simplify the equation.	$y = 4x - 4$.

2 Find the equation of the tangent to the graph of $y = x^3 - 3x^2 + 1$ at the point for which $x = -1$.

The only difference between this example and Example 1 is that you have to find the coordinates of the point on the graph for which $x = -1$.

Differentiate to find the gradient.	If $y = x^3 - 3x^2 + 1$, then $\dfrac{dy}{dx} = 3x^2 - 6x$.
Substitute $x = -1$ to find the required gradient.	When $x = -1$, $\dfrac{dy}{dx} = 3 \times (-1)^2 - 6 \times (-1) = 9$ so the gradient is 9.
Find the coordinates of the point on the curve for which $x = -1$ by substituting $x = -1$ in its equation.	When $x = -1$, $y = (-1)^3 - 3 \times (-1)^2 + 1 = -3$, so the point is $(-1, -3)$.
Find the equation of the line using $y - Y = m(x - X)$.	The tangent has gradient 9 and passes through $(-1, -3)$, so its equation is $y - (-3) = 9(x - (-1))$
Then simplify the equation.	or $y = 9x + 6$.

3 Find the equation of the tangent to the curve $y = 3x^2 - 2x + 1$ which is parallel to the line $y = 10x$.

You need to use the fact that the line $y = 10x$ has gradient 10 to find the point on the curve where the tangent has gradient 10.

Differentiate to find the gradient.	If $y = 3x^2 - 2x + 1$, then $\dfrac{dy}{dx} = 6x - 2$.
Find where the gradient is 10.	$\dfrac{dy}{dx} = 10$ when $6x - 2 = 10$, that is, when $x = 2$.
Find the y-coordinate for $x = 2$.	When $x = 2$, $y = 3 \times 2^2 - 2 \times 2 + 1 = 9$.
Use $y - Y = m(x - X)$ to find the equation of the line.	The tangent has gradient 10 and passes through $(2, 9)$, so its equation is $y - 9 = 10(x - 2)$
Simplify the equation.	or $y = 10x - 11$.

To find the equation of the normal to a curve, you need the extra information that if two lines are at right angles, then the product of their gradients is -1.

4 Find the equation of the normal to the curve $y = x^2 - 2x - 1$ at the point for which $x = 3$. Find the x-coordinate of the point where the normal meets the curve again.

You cannot approach this problem directly. You have to find the gradient of the normal via the gradient of the corresponding tangent.

Differentiate, and find the gradient of the tangent at $x = 3$.	If $y = x^2 - 2x - 1$, then $\dfrac{dy}{dx} = 2x - 2$. At $x = 3$, the tangent gradient is 4.
The tangent and normal are at right angles, so the product of their gradient is -1. Use this to find the gradient of the normal.	Let m be the gradient of the normal. Then $4 \times m = -1$, so $m = -\frac{1}{4}$.
Find the y-coordinate for $x = 3$.	When $x = 3$, $y = 3^2 - 2 \times 3 - 1 = 2$.
Use $y - Y = m(x - X)$ to find the equation of the normal. Simplify the equation.	The normal has gradient $-\frac{1}{4}$ and passes through $(3, 2)$, so its equation is $y - 2 = -\frac{1}{4}(x - 3)$ or $4y = -x + 11$.
To find where this line meets the curve again, solve this equation simultaneously with the equation of the curve.	The line $4y = -x + 11$ meets $y = x^2 - 2x - 1$ where $4(x^2 - 2x - 1) = -x + 11$, that is, $4x^2 - 7x - 15 = 0$, or $(x - 3)(4x + 5) = 0$, that is $x = 3$ or $x = -\frac{5}{4}$.
Reject the solution you do not want. Note that you could have predicted that $x = 3$ was a solution of the simultaneous equations, because it is one of the places that this normal meets the curve.	The point $x = 3$ is already known, so the required value is $x = -\frac{5}{4}$.

5 Find the equation of the tangent and of the normal to $y = x^2(x-2)$ at the point other than the origin where it cuts the x-axis.

Find where the graph of $y = x^2(x-2)$ cuts the x-axis. Recall that the x-axis has equation $y = 0$.	The curve $y = x^2(x-2)$ meets the x-axis at $y = 0$, so $x^2(x-2) = 0$, giving $x = 0$ and $x = 2$. The point away from the origin is $(2,0)$.
Differentiate and find the gradient at $(2,0)$.	$y = x^2(x-2) = x^3 - 2x^2$ $\dfrac{dy}{dx} = 3x^2 - 4x$. At $x = 2$ the gradient is $3 \times 2^2 - 4 \times 2 = 4$.
The tangent has gradient 4 and passes through $(2,0)$.	The equation of the tangent is $y - 0 = 4(x-2)$, that is, $y = 4x - 8$.
The normal is perpendicular to the tangent, so its gradient is $-\frac{1}{4}$. It also passes through $(2,0)$.	The equation of the normal is $y - 0 = -\frac{1}{4}(x-2)$, that is, $4y = -x + 2$.

It often appears more difficult to find the tangent at a point when the x-coordinate is given as a letter.

6 Find the equation of the tangent to the curve $y = \sqrt{x}$ at the point $x = a$, where $a > 0$.

It is important to be clear about what you are doing. The steps are precisely those of Example 2.

Differentiate to find the gradient.	$y = \sqrt{x} = x^{\frac{1}{2}}$ $\dfrac{dy}{dx} = \frac{1}{2}x^{-\frac{1}{2}} = \dfrac{1}{2\sqrt{x}}$

You want the gradient at $x = a$, so substitute $x = a$ in the expression for $\dfrac{dy}{dx}$.

When $x = a$, the gradient is $\dfrac{1}{2\sqrt{a}}$.

Find the coordinates of the point on the curve for which $x = a$ by substituting $x = a$ in its equation.

When $x = a$, $y = \sqrt{a}$, so $\left(a, \sqrt{a}\right)$ is the point through which the tangent passes.

Use the equation $y - Y = m(x - X)$ to find the equation of the line through $\left(a, \sqrt{a}\right)$ with gradient $\dfrac{1}{2\sqrt{a}}$.

Simplify the result.

The equation is
$$y - \sqrt{a} = \frac{1}{2\sqrt{a}}(x - a), \text{ that is,}$$
$$2\sqrt{a}\left(y - \sqrt{a}\right) = (x - a) \text{ or}$$
$$2\sqrt{a}y - 2a = x - a \text{ giving}$$
$$2\sqrt{a}y = x + a.$$

Exercise 4

In questions 1 to 6, find the equation of the tangent to the curve corresponding to the given value of x. Keep your working for questions 7 to 12.

1 $y = x^2$, $x = -1$

2 $y = 2x^2 - 3x + 4$, $x = 0$

3 $y = 2\sqrt{x}$, $x = 9$

4 $y = x^3 - x$, $x = 1$

5 $y = \dfrac{1}{x}$, $x = 2$

6 $y = x^2 - \dfrac{1}{x^2}$, $x = 1$

In questions 7 to 12, find the equation of the normal to the curve corresponding to the given value of x.

7 $y = x^2$, $x = -1$

8 $y = 2x^2 - 3x + 4$, $x = 0$

9 $y = 2\sqrt{x}$, $x = 9$

10 $y = x^3 - x$, $x = 1$

11 $y = \dfrac{1}{x}$, $x = 2$

12 $y = x^2 - \dfrac{1}{x^2}$, $x = 1$

13 Find the equations of the tangent and the normal to $y = x^2(x-3)$ at the point (not the origin) where it cuts the x-axis.

14 Find the equations of the tangent and the normal to the curve $y = x^3 - 2x^2 + x - 1$ at the point where it cuts the y-axis.

15 Find the values of x for which the gradient of the curve $y = x^3 - 6x^2 + 9x - 4$ is zero. Hence find the equations of the tangents which are parallel to the x-axis.

16 Find the equation of the tangent and normal to the curve $y = x^2$ at the point for which $x = a$.

17 Find the equation of the tangent at the point $x = -1$ to the curve $y = x^3 - x$, and find where this tangent meets the curve again.

18 Find the coordinates of the point on the curve $y = 2x + 3x^2 - x^3$ at which the tangent is parallel to the tangent at $x = 2$.

19 Find the equation of the tangent at $x = a$ to the curve $y = x^2 + x + 1$. Hence find the coordinates of the points on the curve such that the tangent passes through the origin.

5 Rate of change

You will need to know

- that the rate of change of y with respect to x is defined to be $\dfrac{dy}{dx}$

- the meaning of displacement

- how to draw and interpret a displacement-time graph

- that velocity means rate of change of displacement with respect to time

- that acceleration means rate of change of velocity with respect to time

- that velocity and acceleration are the gradients of displacement-time and velocity-time graphs respectively

- if you are not told what the rate is with respect to, you should assume it is time.

1 Pat is swimming lengths in a swimming pool. Pat's displacement-time graph is shown in Fig. 5.1, in which the units of time are minutes and the units of distance are metres. (*a*) How long does it take Pat to swim a length? (*b*) What is Pat's velocity during the first minute, during the second minute, and during the sixth minute.

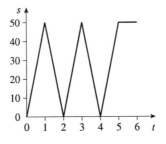

Fig. 5.1

To answer this question you need to make some assumptions about the swimming bath. As Pat moves up and down the bath, it looks as though the length of the bath is 50 metres.

The time taken to swim a length is the time between turns. The positive sloping pieces of graph show when Pat is going up the pool, and the negative parts represent coming back.

(*a*) The time for one length will be the time for which Pat is going in the same direction.	The time for a length is 1 minute.
(*b*) In the first minute Pat's displacement changes by 50 m.	The outward velocity is 50 m min^{-1}.
In the second minute, Pat changes displacement from 50 to 0, that is, by -50 m.	The return velocity is -50 m min^{-1}.
During the sixth minute, the change in displacement is 0 m.	The velocity in the sixth minute is 0 m min^{-1}.

2   The velocity-time graph of a tube train between stops is given in Fig. 5.2. Identify the times at which the acceleration is greatest, the velocity is greatest, and the acceleration is least. The units are metres and seconds.

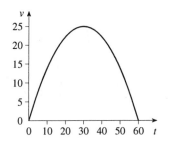

Fig. 5.2

Acceleration is rate of change of velocity, and is given by the gradient of the velocity-time graph.

The maximum acceleration occurs when the gradient is greatest.	The maximum acceleration occurs at time $t = 0$.
The greatest velocity can be read straight from the graph.	The maximum velocity is 25 m s^{-1}.
The minimum acceleration occurs when the gradient is least.	The minimum acceleration occurs at time $t = 60$, that is, after 60 seconds.

There is potential for confusion here because this minimum acceleration is negative, and because the word 'deceleration' is often used to mean negative acceleration. Thus in this case the minimum acceleration occurs when the deceleration is greatest.

3 A particle moves along a straight line in such a way that its displacement s metres after t seconds is given by $s = t^2 + 2t - 1$. Find a formula for the velocity, and calculate the velocity when $t = 2$.

Since velocity is rate of change of displacement, it is given by $\dfrac{\mathrm{d}s}{\mathrm{d}t}$. Therefore, if v denotes velocity, $v = \dfrac{\mathrm{d}s}{\mathrm{d}t}$.

To calculate velocity, differentiate the expression for displacement.	If $s = t^2 + 2t - 1$, then $v = \dfrac{\mathrm{d}s}{\mathrm{d}t} = 2t + 2$.
For velocity at $t = 2$, substitute $t = 2$ into the formula for v.	When $t = 2$, $v = 2 \times 2 + 2 = 6 \text{ m s}^{-1}$.

4   For the first ten seconds the velocity v metres per second of a car t seconds after it has moved away from traffic lights is given by $v = 3t$. Show that the acceleration is constant and find its value.

Since acceleration is rate of change of velocity , it is given by $\dfrac{dv}{dt}$. Therefore, if a denotes acceleration, $a = \dfrac{dv}{dt}$.

To find acceleration, differentiate the expression for velocity.	$v = 3t$ $a = \dfrac{dv}{dt} = 3.$
Acceleration is measured in m s^{-2}.	Therefore the acceleration is constant, 3 m s^{-2}.

5   A particle is thrown vertically into the air. Its displacement s metres from the point of release t seconds after it is thrown is given by $s = 20t - 5t^2$. Find (*a*) the initial velocity of the particle, (*b*) the time at which the particle is momentarily at rest, (*c*) the position of the particle when the velocity is 5 m s^{-1}.

Find a formula for the velocity by differentiating the displacement.	If $s = 20t - 5t^2$, then $v = 20 - 10t$.
(*a*) The initial velocity of the particle is when $t = 0$, so substitute this value in the velocity formula.	When $t = 0$, the initial velocity is $v = 20 - 10 \times 0 = 20$ m s^{-1}.
(*b*) The particle is momentarily at rest when $v = 0$. Use this to find an equation for t and solve it.	When $v = 0$, $20 - 10t = 0$, giving $t = 2$. The velocity is zero after 2 seconds.

(*c*) Find the time at which the velocity is 5 m s^{-1}.	When $v = 5$, $20 - 10t = 5$ giving $t = 1.5$.
Then use this time to find the displacement.	When $t = 1.5$, $s = 20 \times 1.5 - 5 \times (1.5)^2 = 18.75$ Displacement is 18.75 m.

The idea of rate of change applies to situations other than displacement, velocity and acceleration. For example, if you measure the temperature in degrees Centigrade of a cup of tea as it is cooling, then the gradient of the graph of temperature against time gives you the rate of change of temperature with respect to time.

6   The temperature T degrees Centigrade of a cup of coffee t minutes after it is poured is given approximately by the formula $T = 70 - 10t + \frac{1}{2}t^2$. The formula is valid only for $0 \le t \le 10$. Find (*a*) the initial temperature, (*b*) the rate of loss of temperature after 5 minutes. Explain why the formula might only be valid for the first 10 minutes.

The initial temperature is when $t = 0$.	Put $t = 0$. The initial temperature is 70 °C.
For the rate of loss of temperature, you need the rate of change, so differentiate. Then substitute $t = 5$.	$T = 70 - 10t + \frac{1}{2}t^2$, $\dfrac{dT}{dt} = -10 + t$ When $t = 5$, $\dfrac{dT}{dt} = -10 + 5 = -5$.
Notice that $\dfrac{dT}{dt}$ is negative showing that the rate of increase of temperature is negative. To find the rate of loss of temperature, reverse the sign.	The rate of loss of temperature is $5 °\text{C/min}$.

The formula is not likely to work after 10 minutes because it predicts that the temperature starts increasing.

Exercise 5

1   Figure 5.3 shows the displacement-time graph of a mechanical toy moving
     backwards and forwards along a straight line. The units are centimetres and
     seconds.

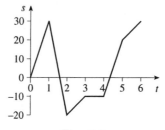

Fig. 5.3

During which periods is the velocity greatest? What is happening in the fourth
second? Calculate the least velocity of the toy.

2   The velocity-time graph of a cork on the surface of a wave is shown in
     Fig. 5.4. The time is measured in seconds, and velocity in cm s^{-1}.

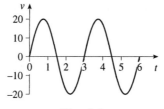

Fig. 5.4

At what times is the acceleration least? When is the acceleration zero?

3   After t seconds the displacement s metres of a particle is given by the formula
     $s = 2t - 3$. Show that its velocity is constant and find its value.

4   The displacement s metres after t seconds of a particle is given by $s = 5t - t^2$,
     calculate the velocity after t seconds. Find the value of t when the velocity is
     zero.

5   After t seconds the displacement s metres of a moving body is given by
     $s = 2 + 6t - t^2$. Find expressions for the velocity and acceleration. Find when
     the velocity is 2 m s^{-1}.

6   The velocity of a moving particle after t seconds is v m s^{-1} where
     $v = 3t^2 - 2t$. Calculate the acceleration after 1 second and after 2 seconds.

7   A stone is thrown vertically upwards. Its displacement s metres from the point of release t seconds after it is thrown is given by $s = 10t - 5t^2$. Find the displacement of the stone when is at the top of its path.

8   A particle moves so that its displacement s in metres after time t seconds is given by $s = t^3 - 9t^2 + 24t - 12$. Find expressions for its velocity and acceleration and find its displacement when the velocity is zero, and when the acceleration is zero.

9   The temperature θ °C of a hot plate t minutes after the power has been switched off is given by $\theta = 3(10 - t)^2 + 20$ for $0 \le t \le 10$. Find (*a*) the initial temperature of the hot plate, and its initial rate of loss of temperature, (*b*) the rate of loss of temperature when $t = 5$ and $t = 10$. What can you deduce from your last answer?

6 Local maxima and minima (1)

You will need to know

- that a stationary point is any point for which $\dfrac{dy}{dx} = 0$

- how to tell whether a stationary point is a local maximum, a local minimum or a point of inflexion by using the sign of $\dfrac{dy}{dx}$ near the stationary point.

You should also know that many people use the words 'maximum' and 'minimum' as shorthand for 'local maximum' and 'local minimum'.

1   Find the stationary points of $y = x^3 - 12x + 3$. (You do not need to distinguish between them.)

The stationary points on the curve are those points for which $\dfrac{dy}{dx} = 0$.

Differentiate to find $\dfrac{dy}{dx}$; put $\dfrac{dy}{dx} = 0$.	If $y = x^3 - 12x + 3$, then $\dfrac{dy}{dx} = 3x^2 - 12$ $\qquad = 3(x-2)(x+2).$
Solve the resulting equation for x.	$\dfrac{dy}{dx} = 0$ for $x = 2$ or $x = -2$.
Stationary points occur at $x = \pm 2$. Find the corresponding y-coordinates by substituting these x-values in the equation $y = x^3 - 12x + 3$.	When $x = 2$, $y = 2^3 - 12 \times 2 + 3 = -13$. Similarly, when $x = -2$, $y = 19$.
Present your results.	The stationary points are $(2, -13)$ and $(-2, 19)$.

28

2 Find the stationary points of $y = x + \dfrac{1}{x}$. (You do not need to distinguish between them.)

The stationary points on the curve are those points for which $\dfrac{dy}{dx} = 0$.

Differentiate to find $\dfrac{dy}{dx}$. You need first to write $\dfrac{1}{x}$ as x^{-1}.	If $y = x + \dfrac{1}{x}$, then $y = x + x^{-1}$ and $\dfrac{dy}{dx} = 1 + (-1) \times x^{-2} = 1 - \dfrac{1}{x^2}$.
Put $\dfrac{dy}{dx} = 0$ for stationary points.	$\dfrac{dy}{dx} = 0$ when $1 - \dfrac{1}{x^2} = 0$.
Solve the resulting equation for x by multiplying both sides by x^2 to clear the fractions.	Therefore $x^2 - 1 = 0$, giving $x = 1$ and $x = -1$.
Stationary points occur at $x = \pm 1$. Find the corresponding y-coordinates by substituting these x-values in the equation $y = x + \dfrac{1}{x}$.	When $x = 1$, $y = 1 + \dfrac{1}{1} = 2$. When $x = -1$, $y = -1 + \dfrac{(-1)}{1} = -2$.
Present your results.	The stationary points are $(1, 1)$ and $(-1, -1)$.

Determining whether a given stationary point is a local maximum, a local minimum, or neither of these, you need to draw, in effect, a very rough sketch of the curve close to the stationary point, using evidence given to you by the sign of the gradient.

3 In Example 1, determine whether each of the stationary points $(2, -13)$ and $(-2, 19)$ for the graph $y = x^3 - 12x + 3$ is a local maximum or a local minimum.

Investigate the sign of $\dfrac{dy}{dx}$ when x is just less than 2.	If x is a little less than 2, $x - 2$ is negative and $x + 2$ is positive. Therefore $3(x - 2)(x + 2)$ is negative.
Investigate the sign of $\dfrac{dy}{dx}$ when x is just greater than 2.	If x is a little greater than 2, $x - 2$ is positive and $x + 2$ is positive. Therefore $3(x - 2)(x + 2)$ is positive.
Collect the conclusions.	Therefore, as x passes through the value 2, $\dfrac{dy}{dx}$ passes from negative to zero to positive.

The method now involves drawing a very rough sketch of that part of the graph close to the turning point. For this case your sketch should have a negative gradient to the left of 2, then zero gradient, followed by a piece with positive gradient.

When $\dfrac{dy}{dx}$ is negative the curve slopes downwards, that is, ↘.	When x is a little less than 2, the gradient is negative and the curve slopes ↘.
When $\dfrac{dy}{dx}$ is zero the curve is horizontal, that is, →.	When x equals 2, the gradient is zero and the curve slopes →.
When $\dfrac{dy}{dx}$ is positive the curve slopes upwards, that is, ↗.	When x is a little greater than 2, the gradient is positive and the curve slopes ↗.

Now put these three arrows together, in order. The shape appears like a minimum.

Around $x = 2$, the shape of the curve is ↘→↗, so at $x = 2$ there is a minimum.

This process is not usually written in such detail. For $x = -2$, the work is shortened.

Investigate the sign of $\dfrac{dy}{dx}$ when x is just less, equal to and greater than -2.

When x is a little less than -2, the gradient is + leading to ↗.
When x equals -2, the gradient is zero and the curve slopes →.
When x is a little greater than -2, the gradient is negative leading to ↘.

Put these arrows together in order to deduce the shape of the graph around $x = -2$.

Around $x = -2$, the shape of the curve is ↗→↘, so at $x = -2$ there is a maximum.

4 In Example 2, determine whether each of the stationary points $(-1, -1)$ and $(1, 1)$ for the graph $y = x + \dfrac{1}{x}$ is a local maximum or a local minimum.

For $x = 1$, find the sign of $\dfrac{dy}{dx}$ when x is just less, equal to and greater than 1.

$\dfrac{dy}{dx} = 1 - \dfrac{1}{x^2}$. When x is just less than 1, the gradient is negative, ↘.
For x equals 1, the gradient is 0, →.
For x just greater than 1, the gradient is positive, ↗.

Put these arrows together in order to deduce the shape of the graph at $x = 1$.

Around $x = 1$, the shape of the curve is ↘→↗, so at $x = 1$ there is a minimum.

For $x = -1$, find the sign of $\dfrac{dy}{dx}$ when x is just less, equal to and greater than -1.	$\dfrac{dy}{dx} = 1 - \dfrac{1}{x^2}$. When x is just less than -1, the gradient is positive, ↗. For x equals -1, the gradient is 0, →. For x just greater than -1, the gradient is negative, ↘.
Put these arrows together in the correct order to find the shape of the graph at $x = -1$.	Around $x = -1$, the shape of the curve is ↗→↘, so at $x = 1$ there is a maximum.

Notice that in this case, the minimum is at $(1,1)$ and the maximum is at $(-1,-1)$, that is, the minimum is greater than the maximum. This is why the terms 'local minimum' and 'local maximum' are sometimes used.

Fig. 6.1 shows a sketch of this graph, and explains why the local minimum is greater than the local maximum. There is a break in the curve as it crosses the y-axis.

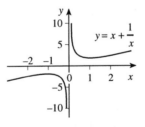

$$y = x + \frac{1}{x}$$

Fig. 6.1

Function notation is often used instead of 'd' notation. The mathematical process does not change.

5   Find the maximum or minimum value of the function $f(x) = 3x^2 - 9x - 2$.

The technique is identical to Examples 3 and 4. Only the notation is different.

Differentiate to find $f'(x)$.	$f(x) = 3x^2 - 9x - 2$, $f'(x) = 6x - 9$.
Put $f'(x) = 0$ for stationary points.	$f'(x) = 0$ when $6x - 9 = 0$, that is, when $x = 1\frac{1}{2}$.
Find the corresponding value of $f(x)$.	$f\left(1\frac{1}{2}\right) = 3 \times \left(1\frac{1}{2}\right)^2 - 9 \times \left(1\frac{1}{2}\right) - 2$ $= -8\frac{3}{4}$.
Find the sign of $f'(x)$ when x is just less, equal to and greater than $1\frac{1}{2}$.	$f'(x) = 6x - 9 = 6\left(x - 1\frac{1}{2}\right)$. When x is just less than $1\frac{1}{2}$, the gradient is negative, $\searrow$. For x equals $1\frac{1}{2}$, the gradient is 0, $\rightarrow$. For x just greater than $1\frac{1}{2}$, the gradient is positive, $\nearrow$.
Put these arrows together to deduce the shape of the graph at $x = 1\frac{1}{2}$.	Around $x = 1\frac{1}{2}$, the shape of the curve is $\searrow \rightarrow \nearrow$, so at $x = 1\frac{1}{2}$ there is a minimum.
State the result.	The function $f(x) = 3x^2 - 9x - 2$ has a minimum of $-8\frac{3}{4}$ (at $x = 1\frac{1}{2}$).

6 Find any stationary points of $f(x) = x^3$, and determine their nature.

Differentiate to find $f'(x)$.	$f(x) = x^3$, $f'(x) = 3x^2$
Put $f'(x) = 0$ for stationary points.	$f'(x) = 0$ when $3x^2 = 0$, that is, when $x = 0$.
Find the corresponding value of $f(x)$.	$f(0) = 0^3 = 0$

Find the sign of $f'(x)$ when x is just less, equal to and greater than 0.	$f'(x) = 3x^2$. When x is just less than 0, the gradient is positive, ↗. For x equals 0, the gradient is 0, →. For x just greater than 0, the gradient is positive, ↗.
Put these arrows together to deduce the shape of the graph at $x = 0$.	Around $x = 0$, the shape of the curve is ↗ → ↗, so at $x = 0$ there is a horizontal point of inflexion.
State the result.	The function $f(x) = x^3$ has a horizontal point of inflexion at $(0,0)$.

Figure 6.2 shows a sketch of the graph of $y = x^3$ with the horizontal point of inflexion at $(0,0)$. The curve follows the shape of the arrows in Example 6.

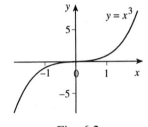

Fig. 6.2

Exercise 6

For each of the following functions, find the values of x at which stationary points occur, and distinguish between them. Find also the corresponding value(s) of the function. Use the notation in which the question is given. You may find it useful to keep your answers for the curve sketching chapter, Chapter 8.

1	$y = x^2 - 6x + 3$	2	$y = 7 - 4x - x^2$
3	$f(x) = 6x - x^2$	4	$f(x) = x^2 + 3x$
5	$y = 2x^2 - x^3$	6	$y = x^3 - 3x - 1$
7	$f(x) = 3x^2 + 2x - 5$	8	$f(x) = 4 - 12x - 3x^2$
9	$y = x(5 - 2x)$	10	$y = x^3 - 12x + 2$

11 $f(x) = 2x^3 - 9x^2 + 12x - 4$

12 $f(x) = 1 + 9x + 3x^2 - x^3$

13 $y = 1 - 3x - 3x^2 - x^3$

14 $y = x^3 - 6x^2 + 12x - 11$

15 $f(x) = x + \dfrac{1}{x} + 2$

16 $f(x) = 2x^3 - 3x^2 - 36x + 6$

17 $y = 6 + 12x - 3x^2 - 2x^3$

18 $y = 3 - x^3$

19 $f(x) = 2x^3 + 3x^2 - 36x + 6$

20 $f(x) = x^3 + 2$

21 $y = x^2 + \dfrac{2}{x}$

22 $y = 2x + \dfrac{8}{x} + 3$

23 $f(x) = x^3 - 5x^2 + 7x - 3$

24 $f(x) = 29 - 27x + 9x^2 - x^3$

25 $y = x^2 - \dfrac{16}{x}$

7   Local maxima and minima (2)

You will need to know

- that if $\dfrac{d^2y}{dx^2} < 0$ at a point for which $\dfrac{dy}{dx} = 0$, then y has a local maximum at that point

- that if $\dfrac{d^2y}{dx^2} > 0$ at a point for which $\dfrac{dy}{dx} = 0$, then y has a local minimum at that point

- that if $\dfrac{d^2y}{dx^2} = 0$ at a point for which $\dfrac{dy}{dx} = 0$, then y could have a local minimum, a local maximum or a horizontal point of inflexion at that point.

You can use the second derivative to tell whether a stationary point is a maximum or a minimum, provided the second derivative is not zero. If $\dfrac{d^2y}{dx^2} = 0$ and $\dfrac{dy}{dx} = 0$ at a point, you cannot use the second derivative method. You must go back to the method of Chapter 6.

1   Find the maximum and minimum values of $y = x^2 - 4x + 3$.

Differentiate to find $\dfrac{dy}{dx}$, put $\dfrac{dy}{dx} = 0$, and solve the resulting equation for x. Find the corresponding y-coordinate.

$y = x^2 - 4x + 3$, $\dfrac{dy}{dx} = 2x - 4$

$\dfrac{dy}{dx} = 0$ when $2x - 4 = 0$, i.e., $x = 2$.

When $x = 2$, $y = 2^2 - 4 \times 2 + 3 = -1$.

To determine whether $(2, -1)$ is a maximum or a minimum, find the value of $\dfrac{d^2y}{dx^2}$ at $x = 2$, and use the evidence at the start of this chapter.

Find $\dfrac{d^2y}{dx^2}$, and substitute $x = 2$. Note that when you substitute $x = 2$, the result is still 2.	$\dfrac{d^2y}{dx^2} = 2$.
Use the information at the beginning of the chapter.	Since at $x = 2$, $\dfrac{d^2y}{dx^2} > 0$, this is a minimum point.
Present the information.	So $(2, -1)$ is a local minimum.

2   Find the maximum and minimum values of $f(x) = 2x^3 - 3x^2$.

Differentiate to find $f'(x)$, put $f'(x) = 0$, and solve the resulting equation for x. Find the corresponding values of the function.	$f(x) = 2x^3 - 3x^2$, $f'(x) = 6x^2 - 6x$ $f'(x) = 0$ when $6x(x-1) = 0$, so $x = 0$ or 1. $f(0) = 0$ and $f(1) = -1$.
Find $f''(x)$, and substitute $x = 0$ to find out whether the second derivative is positive or negative.	$f''(x) = 12x - 6$. Putting $x = 0$ gives $f''(0) = 12 \times 0 - 6 = -6 < 0$. As $f''(0) < 0$ this point is a maximum.
Similarly, find $f''(1)$.	Putting $x = 1$ gives $f''(1) = 12 \times 1 - 6 = 6 > 0$. As $f''(1) > 0$ this point is a minimum.
Present the information.	So $(0, 0)$ is a local maximum, and $(1, -1)$ is a local minimum.

You need to take care with this test for maxima and minima. When it works, it is often very quick and easy to use. However, as the third bullet shows, it doesn't always work. Here are two examples where it fails.

3   Find the maximum and minimum values of $f(x) = x^4$.

Differentiate to find $f'(x)$, put $f'(x) = 0$, and solve the resulting equation for x. Find the corresponding values of the function.	$f(x) = x^4$, $f'(x) = 4x^3$ $f'(x) = 0$ when $4x^3 = 0$, so $x = 0$. Substituting $x = 0$ gives $f(0) = 0$.
Find $f''(x)$, and substitute $x = 0$ to find out whether the second derivative is positive or negative.	$f''(x) = 12x^2$. Putting $x = 0$ gives $f''(0) = 12 \times 0^2 = 0$. As $f''(0) = 0$ the second derivative test gives no further information.

You need to revert to the method of Chapter 6 to find what kind of stationary point there is at $x = 0$.

Find the sign of $f'(x)$ when x is just less, equal to and greater than 0.	$f'(x) = 4x^3$. When x is just less than 0, the gradient is negative, ↘. For x equals 0, the gradient is 0, →. For x just greater than 0, the gradient is positive, ↗.
Put these arrows together to deduce the shape of the graph at $x = 0$.	Around , the shape of the curve is ↘→↗, so at $x = 0$ there is a minimum.

4   Find the maximum and minimum values of $f(x) = x^3$.

Differentiate to find $f'(x)$, put $f'(x) = 0$, and solve the resulting equation for x. Find the corresponding values of the function.	$f(x) = x^3$, $f'(x) = 3x^2$ $f'(x) = 0$ when $3x^2 = 0$, so $x = 0$. Substituting $x = 0$ gives $f(0) = 0$.

Find $f''(x)$, and substitute $x = 0$ to find out whether the second derivative is positive or negative.	$f''(x) = 6x$. Putting $x = 0$ gives $f''(0) = 6 \times 0 = 0$. As $f''(0) = 0$ the second derivative test gives no help.
Find the sign of $f'(x)$ when x is just less, equal to and greater than 0.	$f'(x) = 3x^2$. When x is just less than 0, the gradient is positive, ↗. For x equals 0, the gradient is 0, →. For x just greater than 0, the gradient is positive, ↗.
Put these arrows together to deduce the shape of the graph at $x = 0$.	Around $x = 0$, the shape of the curve is ↗→↗, so at $x = 0$ there is a horizontal point of inflexion.

Examples 3 and 4 show you that different conclusions are possible about the nature of a stationary point when $\dfrac{d^2y}{dx^2} = 0$ at a point for which $\dfrac{dy}{dx} = 0$. Beware! You have to use more information.

Exercise 7

For each of the following functions, find the values of x at which stationary points occur, and distinguish between them. Find also the corresponding value(s) of the function. Use the notation in which the question is given.

1	$y = x(5 - 2x)$	2	$y = x^3 - 12x + 2$
3	$f(x) = 2x^3 - 9x^2 + 12x - 4$	4	$f(x) = 1 + 9x + 3x^2 - x^3$
5	$y = 1 - 3x - 3x^2 - x^3$	6	$y = x^3 - 6x^2 + 12x - 11$
7	$f(x) = 29 - 27x + 9x^2 - x^3$	8	$f(x) = 2x^3 - 3x^2 - 36x + 6$
9	$y = 6 + 12x - 3x^2 - 2x^3$	10	$y = 3 - x^3$
11	$f(x) = 2x^3 + 3x^2 - 36x + 6$	12	$f(x) = x^3 + 2$
13	$y = x^2 + \dfrac{2}{x}$	14	$y = 2x + \dfrac{8}{x} + 3$
15	$f(x) = x + \dfrac{1}{x} + 2$	16	$y = x^2 - \dfrac{16}{x}$

8 Sketching graphs of quadratics and cubics

You will need to know

- that quadratic graphs are all parabolas with shapes shown in Fig. 8.1 below

- that cubic graphs have one of the shapes shown in Fig. 8.2 below.

Fig. 8.1: Possible shapes of quadratic graphs

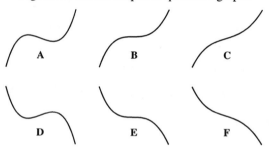

Fig. 8.2: Possible shapes of cubic graphs

The graphs may be squeezed or stretched in either the x or the y-direction, but they will still appear as one of the shapes in Fig. 8.1 or 8.2. However, you need to do some work in order to find which shape the curve is, and where it crosses the axes.

1   Sketch the graph of $y = x^2 - 4x + 3$.

A sketch of a graph should not attempt to be accurate. You need to give an idea of its general shape, together with the coordinates of special points, including those where the graph crosses the axes, and any maxima or minima.

First find where the curve crosses the y-axis by substituting $x = 0$.

When $x = 0$, $y = 0^2 - 4 \times 0 + 3 = 3$, so $(0,3)$ lies on the curve.

If it is easy to do, find where the curve crosses the *x*-axis by putting $y = 0$ and solving the resulting equation.

$y = 0$ when $x^2 - 4x + 3 = 0$, that is, when $(x - 1)(x - 3) = 0$, so $x = 1$ or $x = 3$.

Find any maxima or minima, by finding where $\dfrac{dy}{dx} = 0$.

$\dfrac{dy}{dx} = 2x - 4$, so there is a stationary point when $2x - 4 = 0$, or $x = 2$. When $x = 2$, $y = 2^2 - 4 \times 2 + 3 = -1$.

Find whether this point is a maximum or a minimum.

$\dfrac{d^2 y}{dx^2} = 2$ which is positive, so $(2, -1)$ is a local minimum.

You can now put all this information together to sketch the curve. The fact that the graph has a local minimum tells you that it is of type A in Fig. 8.1.

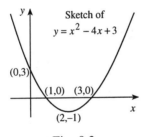

Fig. 8.3

2   Sketch the graph of $y = 3 - 2x - 2x^2$.

First find where the curve crosses the *y*-axis by substituting $x = 0$.

When $x = 0$, $y = 3$, so $(0, 3)$ lies on the curve.

If it is easy to do, find where the curve crosses the *x*-axis by putting $y = 0$ and solving the resulting equation.

$y = 0$ when $3 - 2x - 2x^2 = 0$, that is, when $2x^2 + 2x - 3 = 0$. This has no factors, and will not be taken further.

41

| Find any maxima or minima, by finding where $\dfrac{dy}{dx} = 0$. | $\dfrac{dy}{dx} = -2 - 4x$, so there is a stationary point when $-2 - 4x = 0$, or $x = -\frac{1}{2}$. When $x = -\frac{1}{2}$, $y = 3\frac{1}{2}$. |
| Find whether this point is a maximum or a minimum. | $\dfrac{d^2y}{dx^2} = -4$ which is negative, so $\left(-\frac{1}{2}, 3\frac{1}{2}\right)$ is a local maximum. |

Notice that no attempt has been made in this case to show where the graph crosses the x-axis. Nor has any attempt been made to draw the graph to scale.

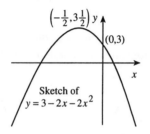

Fig. 8.4

3   Sketch the graph of $y = x^3 - 3x^2 + 3x + 2$.

| First find where the curve crosses the y-axis by substituting $x = 0$. | When $x = 0$, $y = 2$, so $(0, 2)$ lies on the curve. |
| If it is easy to do, find where the curve crosses the x-axis by putting $y = 0$ and solving the resulting equation. | $y = 0$ when $x^3 - 3x^2 + 3x + 2 = 0$, This has no easy factors, so this will not be taken further. |

Find any maxima or minima, by finding where $\dfrac{dy}{dx} = 0$.	$\dfrac{dy}{dx} = 3x^2 - 6x + 3$, so there is a stationary point when $3x^2 - 6x + 3 = 0$, or $3(x-1)^2 = 0$, that is, at $x = 1$. When $x = 1$, $y = 3$.
Use the $\dfrac{d^2y}{dx^2}$ to find whether this point is a maximum or a minimum.	$\dfrac{d^2y}{dx^2} = 6x - 6$. For $x = 1$, $\dfrac{d^2y}{dx^2} = 0$, which gives no information.
Use the method of Chapter 6 instead, involving looking at the gradient just before, and just after $x = 1$.	$\dfrac{dy}{dx} = 3(x-1)^2$. When x is just less than 1, the gradient is positive, $\nearrow$. For x equals 1, the gradient is 0, $\rightarrow$. For x just greater than 1, the gradient is positive, $\nearrow$.
Put these arrows together to deduce the shape of the graph at $x = 1$.	Around $x = 1$, the shape of the curve is $\nearrow \rightarrow \nearrow$, so at $x = 1$ there is a horizontal point of inflexion.

Since there is a horizontal point of inflexion at $x = 1$, and the gradient is otherwise positive, this graph is of type B in Fig. 8.2.

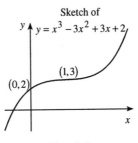

Fig. 8.5

4   Sketch the graph of $f(x) = x^3 + 3x + 1$.

First find where the curve crosses the y-axis by substituting $x = 0$.	$f(0) = 1$, so $(0,1)$ lies on the curve.
If it is easy to do, find where the curve crosses the x-axis by putting $f(x) = 0$ and solving the resulting equation.	$f(x) = 0$ when $x^3 + 3x + 1 = 0$, This has no factors, and will not be taken further.
Find any maxima or minima, by finding where $f'(x) = 0$.	$f'(x) = 3x^2 + 3$, so there is a stationary point when $3x^2 + 3 = 0$, or $3(x^2 + 1) = 0$. There are thus no maxima or minima or horizontal points of inflexion.

As there are no stationary points, the graph is of type C or F in Fig. 8.2. Since $f'(x) = 3(x^2 + 1)$, *the gradient is always positive, so the graph is type C.*

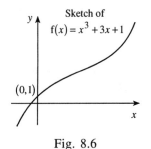

Fig. 8.6

5   Sketch the graph of $f(x) = 12x - 3x^2 - 2x^3$.

First find where the curve crosses the y-axis by substituting $x = 0$.	$f(0) = 0$, so $(0,0)$ lies on the curve.

If it is easy to do, find where the curve crosses the x-axis by putting $f(x) = 0$ and solving the resulting equation.	$f(x) = 0$ when $12x - 3x^2 - 2x^3 = 0$, or $x(12 - 3x - 2x^2) = 0$. The quadratic part does not factorise easily, and will not be taken further. Note however, that there are roots, and that the graph crosses the x-axis three times.
Find any maxima or minima, by finding where $f'(x) = 0$.	$f'(x) = 12 - 6x - 6x^2$, so there is a stationary point when $12 - 6x - 6x^2 = 0$, or $6(x - 1)(x + 2) = 0$, i.e., $x = -2$ or 1. $f(-2) = -20$, and $f(1) = 7$.
Use the $f''(x)$ to find whether these points are maxima or minima.	$f''(x) = -6 - 12x$. $f''(-2) = 18 > 0$ so $(-2, 18)$ is a local minimum. $f''(1) = -18 < 0$ so $(1, 7)$ is a local maximum.

Since this cubic curve has a local minimum followed by a local maximum, it is a curve of type D in Fig. 8.2.

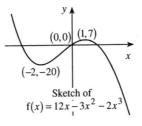

Sketch of
$$f(x) = 12x - 3x^2 - 2x^3$$

Fig. 8.7

45

Exercise 8

Sketch the graphs of each of the following functions. You may already have evidence about them from your work in Chapter 6, but note that not all the question numbers correspond exactly with those of Chapter 6.

1	$y = x^2 - 6x + 3$	2	$y = 7 - 4x - x^2$
3	$f(x) = 6x - x^2$	4	$f(x) = x^2 + 3x$
5	$y = 2x^2 - x^3$	6	$y = x^3 - 3x - 1$
7	$f(x) = 3x^2 + 2x - 5$	8	$f(x) = 4 - 12x - 3x^2$
9	$y = x(5 - 2x)$	10	$y = x^3 - 12x + 2$
11	$f(x) = 2x^3 - 9x^2 + 12x - 4$	12	$f(x) = 1 + 9x + 3x^2 - x^3$
13	$y = 1 - 3x - 3x^2 - x^3$	14	$y = x^3 - 6x^2 + 12x - 11$
15	$f(x) = 29 - 27x + 9x^2 - x^3$	16	$f(x) = 2x^3 - 3x^2 - 36x + 6$
17	$y = 6 + 12x - 3x^2 - 2x^3$	18	$y = 3 - x^3$
19	$f(x) = 2x^3 + 3x^2 - 36x + 6$	20	$f(x) = x^3 + 2$
21	$f(x) = x^3 - 5x^2 + 7x - 3$	22	$y = 3 - 6x - x^3$

9 Points of inflexion

You will need to know

- that a point of inflexion is a point where the gradient was increasing and starts to decrease, or the gradient was decreasing and starts to increase

- that if $\dfrac{d^2y}{dx^2} = 0$ at a point for which $\dfrac{dy}{dx} \neq 0$, then y has a point of inflexion at that point

- that if $\dfrac{d^2y}{dx^2} = 0$ at a point for which $\dfrac{dy}{dx} = 0$, then y could have a horizontal point of inflexion at that point, but it could also have a local minimum or a local maximum.

At a point of inflexion a curve takes one of six shapes shown in Fig. 9.1.

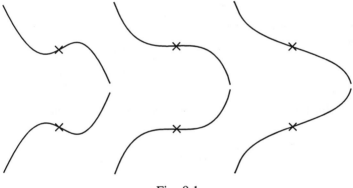

Fig. 9.1

The middle two shapes in each row are horizontal points of inflexion.

1   Find the point of inflexion of $y = x^3 - 4x^2 + 5$.

Differentiate to find $\dfrac{dy}{dx}$ and $\dfrac{d^2y}{dx^2}$.

$\quad y = x^3 - 4x^2 + 5,\ \dfrac{dy}{dx} = 3x^2 - 8x$

$\quad \dfrac{d^2y}{dx^2} = 6x - 8.$

Find where $\dfrac{d^2y}{dx^2} = 0$.	$\dfrac{d^2y}{dx^2} = 0$ when $6x - 8 = 0$, that is, $x = \frac{4}{3}$.
Find the value of $\dfrac{dy}{dx}$ at the point at which $\dfrac{d^2y}{dx^2} = 0$.	When $x = \frac{4}{3}$, $\dfrac{dy}{dx} = 3 \times \left(\dfrac{4}{3}\right)^2 - 8 \times \left(\dfrac{4}{3}\right) = -5\frac{1}{3}$.
Use the information at the beginning of the chapter.	Since at $x = \frac{4}{3}$, $\dfrac{d^2y}{dx^2} = 0$ and $\dfrac{dy}{dx} = -5\frac{1}{3} \neq 0$ there is a point of inflexion at $x = \frac{4}{3}$.
Find the corresponding value of the function.	When $x = \frac{4}{3}$, $y = \left(\dfrac{4}{3}\right)^3 - 4 \times \left(\dfrac{4}{3}\right)^2 + 5 = \dfrac{7}{27}$.
Present the information.	So $\left(\frac{4}{3}, \frac{7}{27}\right)$ is a point of inflexion.

2 Find the points of inflexion on the graph of $y = f(x)$ where $f(x) = x^4 - 216x^2$.

Differentiate to find $f'(x)$ and $f''(x)$.	$f(x) = x^4 - 216x^2$ $f'(x) = 4x^3 - 432x$ $f''(x) = 12x^2 - 432$.
Find where $f''(x) = 0$.	$f''(x) = 0$ when $12x^2 - 432 = 0$, that is, $x^2 - 36 = 0$ or $x = \pm 6$.

Find the value of $f'(x)$ at the points at which $f''(x)=0$.	When $x=6$, $f'(x)=4\times 6^3 -432\times 6=-1728\neq 0$. Similarly, when $x=-6$ $f'(-6)=1728\neq 0$.
Use the information at the beginning of the chapter.	Since at $x=6$ and $x=-6$, $f''(x)=0$ and $f'(x)\neq 0$ there are points of inflexion there.
Find the corresponding value of the function.	When $x=6$, $f(x)=6^4 -216\times 6^2 =-6480$ Similarly, at $x=-6$, $f(x)=-6480$.
Present the information.	So $(6,-6480)$ and $(-6,-6480)$ are points of inflexion.

You need to take care with this test for points of inflexion. When both $\dfrac{dy}{dx}=0$ and $\dfrac{d^2y}{dx^2}=0$, you need to use the method of looking at the gradient before and after the critical points, as illustrated in Chapter 6.

Here is an example, using function notation, where both $f'(x)=0$ and $f''(x)=0$.

3   Find any points of inflexion of $f(x)=x^6$.

Differentiate to find $f'(x)$ and $f''(x)$.	$f(x)=x^6$ $f'(x)=6x^5$ $f''(x)=30x^4$.

Find where $f''(x) = 0$.	$f''(x) = 0$ when $30x^4 = 0$, that is, $x = 0$.
Find the value of $f'(x)$ at the points at which $f''(x) = 0$.	When $x = 0$, $f'(x) = 6 \times 0^5 = 0$.
Find the sign of $f'(x)$ when x is just less, equal to and greater than 0.	$f'(x) = 6x^5$. When x is just less than 0, the gradient is negative, $\searrow$. For x equals 0, the gradient is 0, $\rightarrow$. For x just greater than 0, the gradient is positive, $\nearrow$.
Put these arrows together to deduce the shape of the graph at $x = 0$.	Around , the shape of the curve is $\searrow \rightarrow \nearrow$, so at $x = 0$ there is a minimum.
Present the information.	So there is no point of inflexion on the graph of $f(x) = x^6$.

Exercise 9

For each of the following functions, find the values of x, if any, at which points of inflexion occur. Use the notation in which the question is given.

1 $y = x^3 + 3x^2 + 2x - 1$ 2 $y = 2 - 3x + 6x^2 - x^3$

3 $f(x) = x^4 - 6x^3 - 24x^2 - 6x - 1$ 4 $f(x) = x^3(2 - x)$

5 $y = x^4 - 4x^3 + 6x^2 - 4x$ 6 $y = ax^2 + bx + c$

10 Problems involving maxima and minima

You will need to know

● how to find maximum and minimum values of functions, and to distinguish between them.

The work of this chapter is designed to sharpen your technique in dealing with problems involving maximum and minimum values of functions.

Read Examples 1 and 2, and the commentary which follows them. This shows the general pattern of these problems.

1 A farmer, who has 120 metres of fencing with which to enclose animals, intends to make a rectangular enclosure using an existing wall for one side. Find the maximum area which can be enclosed.

Name the variables.	Let x metres be the length of the side perpendicular to wall, and y metres be the length of the side parallel to the wall. Let A m^2 be the area.
Draw a figure.	 Fig. 10.1
Find an expression for the area.	$A = xy$
Find the relation between x and y.	The length of the fence is 120 metres so $2x + y = 120$

Now find an expression for A, which you want to maximise, in terms of a single variable. So eliminate either x or y; in this example y is being eliminated.

Help yourself to differentiation

| Find y in terms of x, and substitute in the expression for A. | $y = 120 - 2x$
 $A = xy = x(120 - 2x)$. |

Use differentiation to find the maximum value of A.

Differentiate and put $\dfrac{dA}{dx} = 0$. Then solve for x.	$A = x(120 - 2x) = 120x - 2x^2$ $\dfrac{dA}{dx} = 120 - 4x$ $\dfrac{dA}{dx} = 0$ when $x = 30$.
Check that this value of x gives a maximum value of A.	$\dfrac{d^2A}{dx^2} = -4 < 0$, giving a maximum.
Present the final result.	The enclosure of maximum area has dimensions $30\text{ m} \times 60\text{ m}$ giving an area of 1800 m^2.

2   A stained glass window takes the form of a rectangle surmounted by a semicircle. The diameter of the semicircle is equal to the width of the rectangle. The perimeter of the window is 20 metres. The window is made to have a maximum area in order to let in as much light as possible. Find the radius of the semicircle.

| Name the variables. | Let r metres be the radius of the semicircle, and h metres be the height of the rectangle.
 Let $A\text{ m}^2$ be the area. |
| Draw a figure. |
 Fig. 10.2 |

52

Find an expression for the area.	$A = 2rh + \frac{1}{2}\pi r^2$.
Find the relation between r and h.	The perimeter is 20 metres so $2h + 2r + \pi r = 20$.

Now find an expression for A, which you want to maximise, in terms of a single other letter. So eliminate either r or h; in this example h is being eliminated.

Find h in terms of r, and substitute in the expression for A. Simplify the expression for A.	$h = 10 - r - \frac{1}{2}\pi r$ $A = 2rh + \frac{1}{2}\pi r^2$ $\qquad = 2r\left(10 - r - \frac{1}{2}\pi r\right) + \frac{1}{2}\pi r^2$ $\qquad = 20r - 2r^2 - \pi r^2 + \frac{1}{2}\pi r^2$ $\qquad = 20r - 2r^2 - \frac{1}{2}\pi r^2.$

Use differentiation to find the maximum value of A.

Differentiate and put $\dfrac{dA}{dr} = 0$. Then solve for r.	$\dfrac{dA}{dr} = 20 - 4r - \pi r$ $\dfrac{dA}{dr} = 0$ when $20 - 4r - \pi r = 0$, giving $r = \dfrac{20}{4 + \pi}$.
Check that this value of r gives a maximum value of A.	$\dfrac{d^2A}{dr^2} = -4 - \pi < 0$, giving a maximum.
Present the final result.	The radius of the semicircle is $\dfrac{20}{4 + \pi}$ metres.

Examine the common features of Examples 1 and 2. In both of them the quantity that you want to maximise has two variables. In addition, there is a relationship between the two variables. This relation enables you to eliminate one of the variables, so that you can use the maximum and minimum techniques of Chapters 6 and 7.

3 Find the maximum volume of a solid circular cylinder which has a total surface area of A m^2, where A is constant.

Name the variables.	Let r metres be the radius of the cylinder, and h metres be its height. Let V m^3 be the volume.
Find an expression for the volume.	$V = \pi r^2 h$.
Find the relation between r and h.	The area is A m^2 so $$2\pi rh + 2\pi r^2 = A.$$
Find h in terms of r, and substitute in the expression for V. Simplify the expression for V.	$h = \dfrac{A - 2\pi r^2}{2\pi r}$ $$V = \pi r^2 h = \pi r^2 \left(\frac{A - 2\pi r^2}{2\pi r} \right)$$ $$= \tfrac{1}{2} Ar - \pi r^3.$$
Differentiate and put $\dfrac{dV}{dr} = 0$. (Remember that A is a constant.) Then solve for r.	$\dfrac{dV}{dr} = \tfrac{1}{2} A - 3\pi r^2$. $\dfrac{dV}{dr} = 0$ when $\tfrac{1}{2} A - 3\pi r^2 = 0$, giving $$r = \sqrt{\frac{A}{6\pi}}.$$
Check that this value of r gives a maximum value of V.	$\dfrac{d^2 V}{dr^2} = -6\pi r$, and, as r is positive $\dfrac{d^2 V}{dr^2} < 0$ giving a maximum.

Substitute this value of r to find the maximum volume. (The simplification is awkward.)

$$V = \tfrac{1}{2}Ar - \pi r^3$$

$$= r\left(\tfrac{1}{2}A - \pi r^2\right)$$

$$= \sqrt{\frac{A}{6\pi}}\left(\tfrac{1}{2}A - \pi \frac{A}{6\pi}\right)$$

$$= \sqrt{\frac{A}{6\pi}}\left(\tfrac{1}{2}A - \tfrac{1}{6}A\right)$$

$$= \sqrt{\frac{A}{6\pi}}\left(\tfrac{1}{3}A\right) = \frac{A^{\frac{3}{2}}}{3(6\pi)^{\frac{1}{2}}}.$$

Present the final result.

The maximum volume is $\dfrac{A^{\frac{3}{2}}}{3(6\pi)^{\frac{1}{2}}}$ m^3.

Exercise 10

1   A rectangular sheet of metal measures 8 cm by 3 cm. From each corner a square of side x cm is removed, and the flaps so formed are bent up to make a small open box. Show that the volume of the box is $\left(4x^3 - 22x^2 + 24x\right)$ cm^3, and find its maximum value.

2   In question 1, if the width of the metal had been 5 cm instead of 3 cm, what would have been the maximum volume of the box?

3   If $A = xy$ where $3x + y = 18$, find the maximum value of A.

4   If $P = 9x + 8y$ where $xy = 2$, find the minimum value of P, taking x and y to be both positive.

5   Find the maximum area of a rectangle whose perimeter is 32 metres.

6   A piece of wire of length 36 cm is cut and bent to make the shape shown in Fig. 10.3.

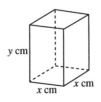

Fig 10.3

Find the dimensions which will maximise the volume outlined by the wire.

55

7 A water tank is to be made, open at the top, on a square base. The volume of the tank is to be 32 m^3. Find the least area of metal sheet which can be used.

8 When an object is projected into the air its height, s metres, after t seconds is given by $s = 98t - 4.9t^2$. Find the greatest height to which it rises.

9 A rectangular sheet of metal measures 20 cm by 15 cm. Equal squares of side x cm are cut from two adjacent corners, and the flaps so formed are bent up to form the tray of a shovel, as in Fig. 10.4.

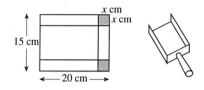

Fig. 10.4

Find the value of x if the volume of the shovel is to be a maximum.

10 Figure 10.5 shows the shape to which some wire is bent to reinforce a package. If the volume of the package is to be a maximum, and the total length of the wire is 60 cm, find the length marked y cm.

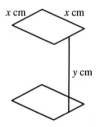

Fig. 10.5

11 A sheet of metal is a square of side 24 cm. From each corner equal squares are removed, and the flaps so formed are bent up to make an open box. Find its maximum volume.

12 A farmer uses some 2 metre hurdles to enclose a rectangular pen of area 200 m^2. If one side of the pen is a river bank which needs no fencing, find the least number of hurdles needed.

13 The surface of a swimming bath has the shape shown in Fig. 10.6. The perimeter of the bath is 132 m. Find the maximum surface area.

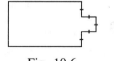

Fig. 10.6

14 Sheet metal with area 216 cm^2 is used for making a closed rectangular box with square ends. Find the dimensions which will give the greatest volume.

15 A total length of 54 cm of wire is used to make the rectangular shape shown in Fig. 10.7. Find the maximum volume outlined by the wire.

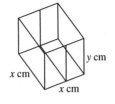

Fig. 10.7

16 An open trough made of wood is in the shape shown in Fig. 10.8. The ends are right-angled isosceles triangles, and are perpendicular to the sides. The total area of wood used is 1728 cm^3. Find the values of x and y which will maximise the volume of the trough.

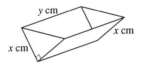

Fig. 10.8

17 A tin box with a lid is being made in the shape of Fig. 10.9. The lid is 1 cm deep. The total area of metal is 960 cm^2. Find the dimensions which give the maximum volume.

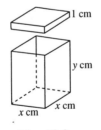

Fig. 10.9

18 A swimming pool is of the shape shown in Fig. 10.10, the radius of each semicircular part being one quarter of the width. The perimeter of the bath is 200 m. Find the width when the area is a maximum. Leave π in your answer.

Fig. 10.10

19 Find in terms of V the minimum surface area of a solid circular cylinder whose volume is V cm^3.

20 A piece of wire of given length is bent to form the perimeter of a sector of a circle. Find the angle between the bounding radii when the area of the sector is a maximum.

11 The composite function rule

You will need to know

● the composite function rule in the form $\dfrac{dy}{dx} = \dfrac{dy}{dz} \times \dfrac{dz}{dx}$.

Written more fully, if y is a function of z where z is a function of x, then $\dfrac{dy}{dx} = \dfrac{dy}{dz} \times \dfrac{dz}{dx}$: this formula is especially easy to remember.

You need the composite function rule, sometimes called the 'function of a function rule', to differentiate functions such as $\sqrt{x^2 + 1}$.

You may know the composite function rule in one of two forms, using 'd' notation or function notion. Most people seem to prefer 'd' notation so that is the notation used in the examples.

1 Differentiate $(2x + 1)^9$.

Notice that you could, if you wish, multiply out the bracket, but that would be very long-winded, and it would not help you to see the structure of the method.

Define the function z.	Let $z = 2x + 1$, so that $y = z^9$.
Find $\dfrac{dy}{dz}$ and $\dfrac{dz}{dx}$.	$\dfrac{dy}{dz} = 9z^8$ and $\dfrac{dz}{dx} = 2$.
Use the formula $\dfrac{dy}{dx} = \dfrac{dy}{dz} \times \dfrac{dz}{dx}$.	$\dfrac{dy}{dx} = 9z^8 \times 2$.
Substitute z, and simplify your answer.	$\dfrac{dy}{dx} = 9(2x+1)^8 \times 2$ $= 18(2x+1)^8.$

2   Differentiate $y = \sqrt{x^2 + 1}$.

Rewrite in index form.

$$y = \left(x^2 + 1\right)^{\frac{1}{2}}.$$

Define the function z.

Let $z = x^2 + 1$, so that $y = z^{\frac{1}{2}}$.

Find $\dfrac{dy}{dz}$ and $\dfrac{dz}{dx}$.

$\dfrac{dy}{dz} = \frac{1}{2}z^{-\frac{1}{2}}$ and $\dfrac{dz}{dx} = 2x$.

Use the formula $\dfrac{dy}{dx} = \dfrac{dy}{dz} \times \dfrac{dz}{dx}$.

$\dfrac{dy}{dx} = \frac{1}{2}z^{-\frac{1}{2}} \times 2x$.

Substitute z, and simplify your answer.

$$\dfrac{dy}{dx} = \frac{1}{2}\left(x^2 + 1\right)^{-\frac{1}{2}} \times 2x$$

$$= \dfrac{x}{\sqrt{x^2 + 1}}.$$

If you study the form of the derivative in Example 1, you will see that in the first, you differentiate a function to the power 9 by writing 9 × the function to the power 8, multiplied by the derivative of that function.

Similarly, in Example 2, you differentiate a function to the power $\frac{1}{2}$ by writing $\frac{1}{2}$ × that function to the power $-\frac{1}{2}$, and then multiplying by the derivative of the function.

You will see this pattern in the following examples. Try as you work to predict mentally what the result will be.

3   Differentiate $\left(3x^2 - 2x + 1\right)^4$.

Define functions y and z.

Let $z = 3x^2 - 2x + 1$, so that $y = z^4$.

Find $\dfrac{dy}{dz}$ and $\dfrac{dz}{dx}$.

$\dfrac{dy}{dz} = 4z^3$ and $\dfrac{dz}{dx} = 6x - 2$.

Use the formula $\dfrac{dy}{dx} = \dfrac{dy}{dz} \times \dfrac{dz}{dx}$.

$\dfrac{dy}{dx} = 4z^3 \times (6x - 2)$.

Substitute z, and simplify your answer.

$\dfrac{dy}{dx} = 4(3x^2 - 2x + 1)^3 \times (6x - 2)$

$= 8(3x - 1)(3x^2 - 2x + 1)^3$.

4 Find the derivative of $\left(x^2 - 1\right)^{\frac{3}{2}}$.

Define functions y and z.

Let $z = x^2 - 1$, so that $y = z^{\frac{3}{2}}$.

Find $\dfrac{dy}{dz}$ and $\dfrac{dz}{dx}$.

$\dfrac{dy}{dz} = \frac{3}{2} z^{\frac{1}{2}}$ and $\dfrac{dz}{dx} = 2x$.

Use the formula $\dfrac{dy}{dx} = \dfrac{dy}{dz} \times \dfrac{dz}{dx}$.

$\dfrac{dy}{dx} = \frac{3}{2} z^{\frac{1}{2}} \times 2x$.

Substitute z, and simplify your answer.

$\dfrac{dy}{dx} = \frac{3}{2}\left(x^2 - 1\right)^{\frac{1}{2}} \times 2x$

$= 3x\left(x^2 - 1\right)^{\frac{1}{2}}$.

5 Find the derivative of $\dfrac{1}{\sqrt{x^2 + 2x}}$.

Define functions y and z, and write the function in power form.

Let $z = x^2 + 2x$, so that $y = z^{-\frac{1}{2}}$.

61

Help yourself to differentiation

Find $\dfrac{dy}{dz}$ and $\dfrac{dz}{dx}$.

$\dfrac{dy}{dz} = -\tfrac{1}{2}z^{-\frac{3}{2}}$ and $\dfrac{dz}{dx} = 2x+2$.

Use the formula $\dfrac{dy}{dx} = \dfrac{dy}{dz} \times \dfrac{dz}{dx}$.

$\dfrac{dy}{dx} = -\tfrac{1}{2}z^{-\frac{3}{2}} \times (2x+2)$.

Substitute z, and simplify your answer.

$\dfrac{dy}{dx} = -\tfrac{1}{2}\left(x^2+2x\right)^{-\frac{3}{2}} \times (2x+2)$

$= -\dfrac{(x+1)}{\left(x^2+2x\right)^{\frac{3}{2}}}.$

Notice that the same pattern works in all these cases. As soon as you are able, drop the substitution and differentiate mentally; but do not make mistakes by doing it!

Exercise 11

Differentiate the following functions. Where it is relevant, a and b are constants.

1   $(2x+1)^2$ 2 $(1-3x)^3$

3   $(2x+5)^{\frac{1}{2}}$ 4 $(4x-1)^{-1}$

5   $(x-3)^2$ 6 $\sqrt{3x+2}$

7   $\left(2x^2+3\right)^3$ 8 $\left(x^2+2\right)^{\frac{3}{2}}$

9   $\sqrt{x^2+2}$ 10 $\left(x^2+2\right)^8$

11   $\sqrt{x+1}$ 12 $\left(3x^2-2x\right)^{10}$

13   $\dfrac{1}{(2x-1)^2}$ 14 $\dfrac{1}{1-2x}$

15   $\sqrt{a+bx}$ 16 $\dfrac{1}{a^2+x^2}$

12 The product and quotient rules

You will need to know

- that product rule for differentiation
- the quotient rule for differentiation.

The product rule for differentiation states that if u and v are functions of x, and if $y = uv$, then

$$\frac{dy}{dx} = u\frac{dv}{dx} + v\frac{du}{dx}.$$

1 Find $\dfrac{dy}{dx}$ when $y = x(x+1)$.

	$y = x(x+1)$
Define functions u and v.	Let $u = x$ and $v = x+1$.
Use the product rule. (Note that you could, if you wished, multiply out the bracket before differentiating.)	$\dfrac{dy}{dx} = x \times 1 + 1 \times (x+1)$ $= 2x + 1.$

2 Find $\dfrac{dy}{dx}$ when $y = \left(x^2 + 1\right)\left(x^2 + 2\right)$.

	$y = \left(x^2 + 1\right)\left(x^2 + 2\right)$
Define functions u and v.	Let $u = x^2 + 1$ and $v = x^2 + 2$.
Differentiate u and v.	$\dfrac{du}{dx} = 2x,\ \dfrac{dv}{dx} = 2x.$

Use the product rule.	$\dfrac{dy}{dx} = \left(x^2 + 1\right) \times 2x + 2x \times \left(x^2 + 2\right)$
Simplify the result by looking for common factors. In this case, $2x$ is a common factor.	$= 2x\left(x^2 + 1 + x^2 + 2\right)$ $= 2x\left(2x^2 + 3\right)$

3 Find $\dfrac{dy}{dx}$ when $y = x\left(1 + x^2\right)^2$.

	$y = x\left(1 + x^2\right)^2$
Define functions u and v.	Let $u = x$ and $v = \left(1 + x^2\right)^2$.
To differentiate v you use the composite function rule, Chapter 11.	$\dfrac{du}{dx} = 1, \quad \dfrac{dv}{dx} = 4x\left(1 + x^2\right).$
Use the product rule.	$\dfrac{dy}{dx} = x \times 4x\left(1 + x^2\right) + 1 \times \left(1 + x^2\right)^2$
Simplify the result by looking for common factors. In this case, $\left(1 + x^2\right)$ is a common factor.	$= \left(1 + x^2\right)\left(4x^2 + 1 + x^2\right)$ $= \left(1 + x^2\right)\left(1 + 5x^2\right).$

In practice you may be able to write down an expression for the result of the differentiation without formally defining functions u and v, and then simplifying if necessary.

4 Differentiate $\left(x^2 + x + 1\right)(x - 1)$.

	Let $y = \left(x^2 + x + 1\right)(x - 1)$.

Use the product rule.

$$\frac{dy}{dx} = \left(x^2 + x + 1\right) \times 1 + (2x+1) \times (x-1).$$

Simplify the result. There are no common factors, so you just have to multiply out and collect terms.

$$= \left(x^2 + x + 1\right) \times 1 + (2x+1) \times (x-1)$$
$$= x^2 + x + 1 + 2x^2 - x - 1$$
$$= 3x^2.$$

5   Differentiate $(2x+1)(3x+2)(4x+3)$.

To differentiate this 'triple product' it is not hard to show that you differentiate the components one at a time, and leave the other two. This gives you three terms to add.

Let $y = (2x+1)(3x+2)(4x+3)$.

Use the product rule.

$$\frac{dy}{dx} = (2x+1)(3x+2) \times 4$$
$$+ (2x+1) \times 3 \times (4x+3)$$
$$+ 2 \times (3x+2)(4x+3)$$

There are no common factors. You have to simplify by brute force.

$$= 72x^2 + 92x + 29.$$

The quotient rule states that if u and v are functions of x, and if $y = \dfrac{u}{v}$, then

$$\frac{dy}{dx} = \frac{v\dfrac{du}{dx} - u\dfrac{dv}{dx}}{v^2}.$$

6   Find $\dfrac{dy}{dx}$ when $y = \dfrac{3x}{2x+1}$.

$$\frac{3x}{2x+1}$$

Define functions u and v.

Let $u = 3x$ and $v = 2x+1$.

Differentiate u and v.

$$\frac{du}{dx} = 3, \quad \frac{dv}{dx} = 2.$$

Use the quotient rule.

$$\frac{dy}{dx} = \frac{(2x+1)\times 3 - 3x \times 2}{(2x+1)^2}$$

Simplify by multiplying out the brackets and collecting like terms.

$$= \frac{3}{(2x+1)^2}.$$

7 Find $\frac{dy}{dx}$ when $y = \frac{2x^2 + x}{x^2 + 1}$.

$$y = \frac{2x^2 + x}{x^2 + 1}$$

Define functions u and v.

Let $u = 2x^2 + x$ and $v = x^2 + 1$.

Differentiate u and v.

$$\frac{du}{dx} = 4x+1, \quad \frac{dv}{dx} = 2x.$$

Use the quotient rule.

$$\frac{dy}{dx} = \frac{(x^2+1)(4x+1) - (2x^2+x)2x}{(x^2+1)^2}.$$

Multiply out the brackets in the numerator and collect like terms.

$$\frac{dy}{dx} = \frac{4x+1-x^2}{(x^2+1)^2}.$$

The product and quotient rules

Simplifying the result can sometimes be harder than the original differentiation. You need to think clearly about what you have to do. It is best to write all the powers as positive before starting to simplify.

8 Find $\dfrac{dy}{dx}$ when $y = \dfrac{\sqrt{x}}{2x+1}$.

$$y = \frac{\sqrt{x}}{2x+1}$$

Define functions u and v.

Let $u = \sqrt{x}$ and $v = 2x+1$.

Differentiate u and v.

$$\frac{du}{dx} = \frac{1}{2}x^{-\frac{1}{2}} = \frac{1}{2x^{\frac{1}{2}}}, \quad \frac{dv}{dx} = 2.$$

Use the quotient rule.

$$\frac{dy}{dx} = \frac{(2x+1)\dfrac{1}{2x^{\frac{1}{2}}} - x^{\frac{1}{2}} \times 2}{(2x+1)^2}.$$

Multiply numerator and denominator by $2x^{\frac{1}{2}}$ to simplify.

$$\frac{dy}{dx} = \frac{(2x+1) - 4x}{2x^{\frac{1}{2}}(2x+1)^2} = \frac{1-2x}{2x^{\frac{1}{2}}(2x+1)^2}.$$

You will often have to use the composite function (function of a function) rule in the process of using the quotient rule.

9 Differentiate $y = \dfrac{2x-1}{(3x+1)^2}$.

$$y = \frac{2x-1}{(3x+1)^2}$$

Define functions u and v.

Let $u = 2x-1$ and $v = (3x+1)^2$.

Help yourself to differentiation

Differentiate u and v. Differentiating $v = (3x+1)^2$ needs the composite function rule.	$\dfrac{du}{dx} = 2$. $\dfrac{dv}{dx} = 2(3x+1) \times 3 = 6(3x+1)$.
Use the quotient rule.	$\dfrac{dy}{dx} = \dfrac{(3x+1)^2 2 - (2x-1)6(3x+1)}{(3x+1)^4}$.
Simplify.	$\dfrac{dy}{dx} = \dfrac{2(3x+1)^2 - 6(2x-1)(3x+1)}{(3x+1)^4}$ $= \dfrac{2(3x+1) - 6(2x-1)}{(3x+1)^3}$ $= \dfrac{-6x+8}{(3x+1)^3}$.

Using the product and quotient rules is usually straightforward. Sometimes, however, the simplification which follows can be tricky. In the answers to this chapter, therefore, there appear two versions: the first is what you get immediately you use the product or quotient rule; the second is what you get when you simplify the result. If you get the first answer but not the second, then you know that you need to brush up on your simplification skills.

Exercise 12

Use the product rule to differentiate the following functions with respect to x. Simplify your answers.

1. $(2x+3)(3x+4)$
2. $(x^2-1)(2x+1)$
3. $(x^2-3x+2)(\frac{1}{2}x+1)$
4. $(x^3-1)(x^3+1)$
5. $(2x-3)(2x^2-5)$
6. $(x-1)(x^3+x^2+x+1)$
7. $(x^2+2x)(2x^2-3x)$
8. $(x+1)\sqrt{x}$
9. $(x+2)(x^2-2x+4)$
10. $(x-3)(x^2+3x+9)$
11. $(x+1)(x^2+1)(x^3+1)$
12. $(ax+b)(ax^2+b)$

68

Use the quotient rule to differentiate the following functions with respect to x.
Simplify your answers.

13 $\dfrac{2}{1+x}$ **14** $\dfrac{3}{1-2x^2}$

15 $\dfrac{x}{x-1}$ **16** $\dfrac{x}{x^2+1}$

17 $\dfrac{4+x}{4-x}$ **18** $y=\dfrac{1+5x}{5-x}$

19 $\dfrac{1-x^2}{1+x^2}$ **20** $\dfrac{1+x^2}{1-x^2}$

21 $\dfrac{x}{(1+2x)^2}$ **22** $\dfrac{2x+1}{(x+2)^2}$

23 $\dfrac{x}{(3x+2)^3}$ **24** $\dfrac{x}{(x+3)^4}$

25 $\dfrac{\sqrt{x^2+1}}{x+1}$ **26** $\dfrac{2x+1}{\sqrt{x^2+1}}$

13 The trigonometric functions

You will need to know

- that $\tan x = \dfrac{\sin x}{\cos x}$, and similar relationships

- that in the following three results, x is in radians

- that the derivative of $\sin x$ is $\cos x$

- that the derivative of $\cos x$ is $-\sin x$

- that the derivative of $\tan x$ is $\sec^2 x$.

In the following examples it is assumed that you know the three differentiation rules, the composite function rule, the product and the quotient rule, and that you are proficient at solving trigonometric equations.

1 Find $\dfrac{dy}{dx}$ when $y = \sin 2x$.

This is an example of the composite function rule. It may be easier to follow if you write in the form $y = \sin(2x)$.

	$y = \sin 2x$
Define the function z.	Let $z = 2x$, so that $y = \sin z$.
Find $\dfrac{dy}{dz}$ and $\dfrac{dz}{dx}$.	$\dfrac{dy}{dz} = \cos z$ and $\dfrac{dz}{dx} = 2$.
Use the formula $\dfrac{dy}{dx} = \dfrac{dy}{dz} \times \dfrac{dz}{dx}$.	$\dfrac{dy}{dx} = \cos z \times 2$.
Substitute z, and simplify your answer.	$\dfrac{dy}{dx} = 2\cos 2x$.

In the following examples it will be assumed that you can use the composite function rule mentally, without writing out the details of the substitution.

2 Find $\dfrac{dy}{dx}$ when $y = \tan\left(x^2 + 1\right)$.

$$y = \tan\left(x^2 + 1\right)$$

Use the composite function rule mentally.

$$\frac{dy}{dx} = \sec^2\left(x^2 + 1\right) \times 2x$$

$$= 2x\sec^2\left(x^2 + 1\right).$$

3 Differentiate $\cos^2 x$.

You need to note that $\cos^2 x$ means $(\cos x)^2$ in order to differentiate. In this example, this is written explicitly, but it will not be in future examples

$$y = \cos^2 x = (\cos x)^2$$

Use the composite function rule mentally.

$$\frac{dy}{dx} = 2\cos x \times (-\sin x)$$

$$= -2\sin x \cos x.$$

You can also expect to use the product and quotient rules.

4 Differentiate $\sin 2x \cos 2x$.

Let $y = \sin 2x \cos 2x$.

Use the product rule, together with the composite function rule.

$$\frac{dy}{dx} = \sin 2x \times (-\sin 2x) \times 2$$

$$+ \cos 2x \times \cos 2x \times 2$$

$$= 2\cos^2 2x - 2\sin^2 2x.$$

5 Differentiate $\sec x$.

> *You need to write* $\sec x = \dfrac{1}{\cos x}$ *and use the quotient rule.*

	Let $y = \sec x = \dfrac{1}{\cos x}$.
Use the quotient rule.	$\dfrac{dy}{dx} = \dfrac{\cos x \times 0 - 1 \times (-\sin x)}{\cos^2 x}$
Simplify your answer.	$= \dfrac{1}{\cos x} \times \dfrac{\sin x}{\cos x} = \sec x \tan x.$

6 Find the maximum and minimum values of $y = 3\sin x + 4\cos x$ in the interval $0 \le x \le 2\pi$.

Differentiate to find $\dfrac{dy}{dx}$, put $\dfrac{dy}{dx} = 0$, and solve the resulting equation for x.	$\dfrac{dy}{dx} = 3\cos x - 4\sin x.$ $\dfrac{dy}{dx} = 0$ when $3\cos x - 4\sin x = 0,$ that is, when $\dfrac{\sin x}{\cos x} = \tan x = \frac{3}{4}.$ So $x = 0.644\ldots, 3.785\ldots$ correct to 3 decimal places.
Find the corresponding values of the function.	When $\tan x = \frac{3}{4}$ and $x = 0.644\ldots,$ $\sin x = \frac{3}{5}$ and $\cos x = \frac{4}{5}$. Then $y = 5.$ When $\tan x = \frac{3}{4}$ and $x = 3.785\ldots,$ $\sin x = -\frac{3}{5}$, $\cos x = -\frac{4}{5}$, so $y = -5.$

Find $\dfrac{d^2y}{dx^2}$, and substitute these values of x into it to find out whether the second derivative is positive or negative.

$\dfrac{d^2y}{dx^2} = -3\sin x - 4\cos x$. Since the value of $\dfrac{d^2y}{dx^2}$ is equal to $-y$, when $y = 5$, $\dfrac{d^2y}{dx^2} = -5 < 0$ giving a maximum. When $y = -5$, $\dfrac{d^2y}{dx^2} = 5 > 0$ giving a minimum.

Present the results.

$y = 3\sin x + 4\cos x$ has a maximum of 5 when $x = 0.644...$, and a minimum of -5 when $x = 3.785...$.

There are alternative trigonometric ways to do the last example without calculus.

7   Find the equation of the normal to the curve $y = x\sin x$ at the point $x = \pi$.

Differentiate, and find the gradient of the tangent at $x = \pi$.

$y = x\sin x$, so $\dfrac{dy}{dx} = x\cos x + \sin x$.

At $x = \pi$, $\dfrac{dy}{dx} = \pi\cos\pi + \sin\pi = -\pi$, so the gradient of the tangent is $-\pi$.

The tangent and normal are at right angles, so the product of their gradient is -1. Use this to find the gradient of the normal.

Let m be the gradient of the normal. Then $-\pi \times m = -1$, so $m = \dfrac{1}{\pi}$.

Find the y-coordinate for $x = \pi$.

When $x = \pi$, $y = \pi\sin\pi = 0$.

Use $y - Y = m(x - X)$ to find the equation of the normal and simplify it.

The normal is $y - 0 = \dfrac{1}{\pi}(x - \pi)$, that is $\pi y = x - \pi$.

8 A particle moves up and down in a straight line in such a way that its height *h* metres at time *t* seconds is given by the equation $h = 3\cos 2t$. Find the velocity of the particle after 2 seconds, and indicate whether it is moving towards the origin, or away from it.

To calculate velocity, differentiate the expression for displacement.	Let the velocity be v ms^{-1}. Then $$v = \frac{dh}{dt} = -6\sin 2t.$$
Find the velocity at 2 seconds by substituting $t = 2$.	When $t = 2$, $v = -6\sin 4 = 4.541...$. The velocity is $4.541...$ ms^{-1}.

To find whether the particle is moving towards or away from the origin, you need to find its displacement as well as its velocity. If the displacement is negative, and the velocity is positive, or vice versa, it will be moving towards the origin. If they are both positive or both negative it is moving away.

Calculate the displacement when $t = 2$.	At $t = 2$, $h = 3\cos 4 = -1.961...$.
Present the conclusion.	Since the displacement is negative and the velocity is positive, the particle is moving towards the origin.

Exercise 13

In questions 1 to 20, differentiate the following functions with respect to *x*.

1	$4\cos x$	**2**	$\sin 5x$
3	$\sin \frac{1}{2}x$	**4**	$\tan 2x$
5	$2\cos 3x + 3\sin 3x$	**6**	$2\cos \frac{1}{2}x - \sin \frac{1}{2}x$
7	$\sin(2x + \pi)$	**8**	$\cos \frac{1}{2}(\pi - x)$
9	$2\sin^2 x$	**10**	$\cos^2 5x$
11	$\sin^3 \frac{1}{2}x$	**12**	$\tan^2 3x$
13	$x\cos 2x$	**14**	$x^2 \tan \frac{1}{2}x$
15	$x\sin^2 x$	**16**	$x\sin x + \cos x$

17 $\dfrac{\sin x}{x}$

18 $\dfrac{1}{1+\cos 2x}$

19 $\dfrac{1}{\sin x}$

20 $\dfrac{\sqrt{\cos x}}{x}$

21 Find the maximum and minimum values of the function $y = \sin x - \cos x$ in the interval $0 \le x \le 2\pi$.

22 Find the equation of the tangent and the normal to the graph of $y = \tan x$ at the point for which $x = -\tfrac{1}{4}\pi$.

23 Find where the tangent to the curve $y = \dfrac{\sin x}{x}$ at the point for which $x = \tfrac{1}{2}\pi$ meets the y-axis.

24 At which points on the graph of $y = \cos 2x$ in the interval $-\pi \le x \le \pi$ is the gradient of the tangent equal to 1?

25 The displacement x cm of a toy oscillating up and down on the end of a spring after t seconds is given by $x = 10\sin 5t$. Calculate the velocity and acceleration of the toy after 1 second. Find the displacement of the toy at the time when it is first instantaneously at rest.

26 The height x metres of the level of the water above the sea floor is given by $x = 5 + 5\cos\left(\tfrac{1}{6}\pi t\right)$ where t is measured in hours. Find the velocity of the water level when it is rising fastest. At what time is this?

14 The exponential and logarithmic functions

You will need to know

● that the derivative of e^x is e^x

● that $\ln x$ is defined only for $x > 0$

● that the derivative of $\ln x$ is $\dfrac{1}{x}$

● the shape of the graph of $y = e^x$

● the shape of the graph of $y = \ln x$.

In the following examples it is assumed that you are familiar with the three differentiation rules, the composite function, product and quotient rules, and that you are proficient at manipulating exponential and logarithmic functions.

1   Find $\dfrac{dy}{dx}$ when $y = e^{2x}$.

This is an example where you need the composite function rule.

$$y = e^{2x}$$

Define the function z.

Let $z = 2x$, so that $y = e^z$.

Find $\dfrac{dy}{dz}$ and $\dfrac{dz}{dx}$.

$\dfrac{dy}{dz} = e^z$ and $\dfrac{dz}{dx} = 2$.

Use the formula $\dfrac{dy}{dx} = \dfrac{dy}{dz} \times \dfrac{dz}{dx}$.

$\dfrac{dy}{dx} = e^z \times 2$.

Substitute z, and simplify your answer.

$\dfrac{dy}{dx} = 2e^{2x}$.

2 Find $\dfrac{dy}{dx}$ when $y = \ln 3x$.

This is another example where you need the composite function rule.

	$y = \ln 3x$
Define the function z.	Let $z = 3x$, so that $y = \ln z$.
Find $\dfrac{dy}{dz}$ and $\dfrac{dz}{dx}$.	$\dfrac{dy}{dz} = \dfrac{1}{z}$ and $\dfrac{dz}{dx} = 3$.
Use the formula $\dfrac{dy}{dx} = \dfrac{dy}{dz} \times \dfrac{dz}{dx}$	$\dfrac{dy}{dx} = \dfrac{1}{z} \times 3$.
Substitute z, and simplify your answer.	$\dfrac{dy}{dx} = \dfrac{1}{3x} \times 3 = \dfrac{1}{x}$.

At first sight this result is surprising. However, note that $\ln 3x = \ln 3 + \ln x$ so that $\ln 3x$ differs from $\ln x$ by a constant.

In the following examples it will be assumed that you can use the composite function rule mentally, without writing out the details of the substitution.

3 Differentiate $y = xe^{-x^2}$.

Define y.	$y = xe^{-x^2}$.
Use the product rule, and the composite function rule mentally.	$\dfrac{dy}{dx} = x \times e^{-x^2} \times -2x + 1 \times e^{-x^2}$.

Help yourself to differentiation

Simplify the result.	$\dfrac{dy}{dx} = -2x^2 e^{-x^2} + e^{-x^2}$
	$= e^{-x^2}\left(1 - 2x^2\right).$

4 Find $f'(x)$ when $f(x) = \ln\left(1 + x^2\right)$.

	$f(x) = \ln\left(1 + x^2\right)$
Use the composite function rule mentally.	$f'(x) = \dfrac{1}{1+x^2} \times 2x = \dfrac{2x}{1+x^2}.$

5 Differentiate $\ln x^4$.

Two methods are given for this problem. The first is similar to the previous examples, but the second is neater.

Define a function.	Let $y = \ln x^4$.
Method 1. Use the composite function rule.	$\dfrac{dy}{dx} = \dfrac{4x^3}{x^4}$
	$= \dfrac{4}{x}.$
Method 2. Use one of the properties of the logarithm function to simplify before you differentiate.	$y = \ln x^4 = 4\ln x$, so $\dfrac{dy}{dx} = \dfrac{4}{x}.$

6   Sketch the graph of $y = \dfrac{\ln x}{x}$ for $x > 0$.

Note that $\ln x$ *is defined only for* $x > 0$, *so the graph does not exist for* $x \le 0$.

First find where the curve crosses the y-axis by substituting $x = 0$.	The curve does not exist when $x = 0$, so it does not cross the x-axis.
If it is easy to do, find where the curve crosses the x-axis by putting $f(x) = 0$ and solving the resulting equation.	$\dfrac{\ln x}{x} = 0$ when $x = 1$ so the point $(1, 0)$ lies on the curve.
Find any maxima or minima, by finding where $\dfrac{dy}{dx} = 0$, and use the quotient rule to find $\dfrac{dy}{dx}$.	$\dfrac{dy}{dx} = \dfrac{x \times \dfrac{1}{x} - \ln x \times 1}{x^2} = \dfrac{1 - \ln x}{x^2}$ $\dfrac{dy}{dx} = 0$ when $1 - \ln x = 0$, so $x = e$.
Find the corresponding value of y.	When $x = e$, $y = \dfrac{\ln e}{e} = \dfrac{1}{e}$.
Use the $\dfrac{d^2y}{dx^2}$ to find whether this point is a maximum or a minimum.	$\dfrac{d^2y}{dx^2} = \dfrac{x^2 \times \left(-\dfrac{1}{x}\right) - (1 - \ln x) \times 2x}{x^4}$.

Note that it is not worth simplifying this expression for $\dfrac{d^2y}{dx^2}$, *because you actually want the value of* $\dfrac{d^2y}{dx^2}$ *when* $x = e$.

Substitute $x = e$ in $\dfrac{d^2y}{dx^2}$, to find whether it is positive or negative.	$\dfrac{d^2y}{dx^2} = -\dfrac{1}{e^3} < 0$, so $\left(e, \dfrac{1}{e}\right)$ is a maximum.

You must check on the behaviour of the graph for very large positive values of x, and for values of x which are positive but very small.

Check the behaviour of y when x is very large and positive.	For very large positive values of x, $\ln x$ and x are both large and positive, but x is much bigger than $\ln x$, and $\dfrac{\ln x}{x} \to 0$.
Check the behaviour of y when x is very small and positive.	For very small positive values of x, $\ln x$ is large and negative and x is small and positive, so $\dfrac{\ln x}{x}$ is very large and negative.
You can now produce the sketch shown in Fig. 14.1, which is not to scale.	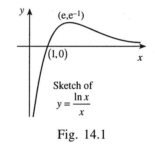

Fig. 14.1

7　Find where the normal at $(1, e)$ to the graph of $y = e^x$ meets the x- and y-axes.

Differentiate, and find the gradient of the tangent at $(1, e)$.	$y = e^x$, so $\dfrac{dy}{dx} = e^x$. At $(1, e)$, $\dfrac{dy}{dx} = e^1 = e$, so the gradient of the tangent is e.
The tangent and normal are at right angles, so the product of their gradients is -1. Use this to find the gradient of the normal.	Let m be the gradient of the normal. Then $e \times m = -1$, so $m = -\dfrac{1}{e}$.

Use $y - Y = m(x - X)$ to find the equation of the normal.	The normal has gradient $-\dfrac{1}{e}$ and passes through $(1, e)$, so its equation is $y - e = -\dfrac{1}{e}(x - 1)$.
Simplify the equation.	The equation of the normal is $y e - e^2 = -x + 1$.
Put $x = 0$ to find where this line meets the y-axis.	$y e - e^2 = -x + 1$ meets the y-axis at $\left(0, e + \dfrac{1}{e}\right)$.
Put $y = 0$ to find where this line meets the x-axis.	$y e - e^2 = -x + 1$ meets the x-axis at $\left(1 + e^2, 0\right)$.

8 A particle oscillates in a straight line in such a way that its displacement x metres at time t seconds is given by the equation $x = Ae^{-t} \cos t$. Find the velocity and acceleration of the particle for the first time it is at the origin after $t = 0$.

Find when the particle is at the origin by putting $x = 0$ and solving for t.	The particle is at the origin when $x = 0$, that is, when $Ae^{-t} \cos t = 0$. Thus, $\cos t = 0$, and the first positive solution is $t = \tfrac{1}{2}\pi$.
Since $v = \dfrac{dx}{dt}$, differentiate to find v.	$v = \dfrac{dx}{dt} = -Ae^{-t} \cos t - Ae^{-t} \sin t$.
Since $a = \dfrac{dv}{dt}$, differentiate to find a.	$a = \dfrac{dv}{dt} = 2Ae^{-t} \sin t$.

| Substitute $t = \frac{1}{2}\pi$ to find the velocity and acceleration. | When $t = \frac{1}{2}\pi$, $v = -Ae^{-\frac{1}{2}\pi}$ m s^{-1}. When $t = \frac{1}{2}\pi$, $a = 2Ae^{-\frac{1}{2}\pi}$ m s^{-2}. |

Exercise 14

In questions 1 to 20, differentiate the following functions with respect to x.

1 e^{4x} **2** $4e^{\frac{1}{4}x}$

3 e^{2x^2} **4** $3e^{-2x}$

5 e^{3-x} **6** $-2e^{-\frac{1}{2}x}$

7 $\ln 3x$ **8** $\ln x^2$

9 $\ln(2x+3)$ **10** $\ln\left(x^2 + 2x\right)$

11 $\ln\left(e^x\right)$ **12** $e^{\ln x}$

13 $\ln(\cos x)$ **14** $\ln 3x^2$

15 $\ln\left(px^2 + qx + r\right)$ **16** $\ln\sqrt{x}$

17 $x^2 e^{-x}$ **18** $x\ln x - x$

19 $\ln\left(\dfrac{2+x}{2-x}\right)$ **20** $\ln\left(\dfrac{a-bx}{a+bx}\right)$

21 Find where the gradient of the graph of $y = e^{-2x}$ is equal to -1.

22 Find the maximum value of the function $y = xe^{-x}$.

23 Find the first maximum value of $y = e^{-x}\sin x$ and show that the values of successive maxima are in geometric progression. Find the common ratio of this geometric progression.

24 The temperature θ in °C at time t minutes of a liquid cooling is given by $\theta = 20 + 60e^{-0.1t}$. Find when the temperature is $26\,°C$, and find the rate of cooling at that time.

25 The population p of the world is increasing exponentially and is believed to obey the law $p = Ae^{kt}$ where A and k are constants. Find the time for the population to reach $2A$ and find the rate of change of population at that time.

26 Find the x-values of the points of inflexion of the graph of $y = e^{-x^2}$.

27 Find the x-values of the points of inflexion of the graph of $y = e^{-\frac{x^2}{2\sigma^2}}$ where σ is a constant.

15 Implicit differentiation

You will need to know

- what an implicit function is, and how it differs from an explicit function

- that the derivative of y with respect to x is $\dfrac{dy}{dx}$

- that the derivative of $f(y)$ with respect to x is $f'(y)\dfrac{dy}{dx}$.

Not all curves have equations of the form $y = f(x)$. For example, a circle with centre (a,b) and radius r has equation $(x-a)^2 + (y-b)^2 = r^2$. You could put this equation in the form $y = b \pm \sqrt{r^2 - (x-a)^2}$, but it is messy, and it is preferable to be able to work with the equation in its original form.

Here are some introductory examples.

1 Differentiate the equation $2x + 3y + 4 = 0$.

This is an example where you could easily write the equation explicitly in the form $y = \ldots\ldots$

$$2x + 3y + 4 = 0$$

Differentiate term by term. The derivative of y with respect to x is $\dfrac{dy}{dx}$.

$$\frac{d}{dx}(2x) + \frac{d}{dx}(3y) + \frac{d}{dx}(4) = \frac{d}{dx}(0)$$

$$2 + 3\frac{dy}{dx} = 0$$

Solve this equation for $\dfrac{dy}{dx}$.

$$\frac{dy}{dx} = -\frac{2}{3}.$$

This is what you would have obtained if you had started by writing $y = \ldots\ldots$

2 Differentiate the product xy with respect to x.

This is a product. Use the product rule in the usual way. If you wish, think of the substitution $u = x$ and $v = y$ in the product rule formula.	$\dfrac{\mathrm{d}}{\mathrm{d}x}(xy) = x \times \dfrac{\mathrm{d}}{\mathrm{d}x}(y) + y\dfrac{\mathrm{d}}{\mathrm{d}x}(x)$ $= x\dfrac{\mathrm{d}y}{\mathrm{d}x} + y.$

3 Differentiate $\cos y$ with respect to x.

This is an example of a composite function. The cosine is a function of y where y is a function of x.

Use the composite function rule. Let $z = \cos y$. Then $\dfrac{\mathrm{d}z}{\mathrm{d}x} = \dfrac{\mathrm{d}z}{\mathrm{d}y} \times \dfrac{\mathrm{d}y}{\mathrm{d}x}$.	$\dfrac{\mathrm{d}}{\mathrm{d}x}(\cos y) = \dfrac{\mathrm{d}}{\mathrm{d}y}(\cos y) \times \dfrac{\mathrm{d}y}{\mathrm{d}x}$ $= -\sin y \times \dfrac{\mathrm{d}y}{\mathrm{d}x}.$

Example 3 shows the use of the composite function rule in differentiating $\mathrm{f}(y)$ with respect to x.

$$\frac{\mathrm{d}}{\mathrm{d}x}\big(\mathrm{f}(y)\big) = \frac{\mathrm{d}}{\mathrm{d}y}\big(\mathrm{f}(y)\big) \times \frac{\mathrm{d}y}{\mathrm{d}x} = \mathrm{f}'(y)\frac{\mathrm{d}y}{\mathrm{d}x}$$

4 Find $\dfrac{\mathrm{d}y}{\mathrm{d}x}$ in terms of x and y when $xy + 2y = 1 + x$.

	$xy + 2y = 1 + x$
Differentiate term by term.	$\left(x\dfrac{\mathrm{d}y}{\mathrm{d}x} + y\right) + 2\dfrac{\mathrm{d}y}{\mathrm{d}x} = 0 + 1.$
Solve for $\dfrac{\mathrm{d}y}{\mathrm{d}x}$.	$\dfrac{\mathrm{d}y}{\mathrm{d}x} = \dfrac{1-y}{x+2}.$

5   Find the gradient at $(-1, 7)$ on the circle $x^2 + y^2 - 4x - 6y - 12 = 0$.

$$x^2 + y^2 - 4x - 6y - 12 = 0$$

Differentiate term by term.

$$2x + 2y\frac{dy}{dx} - 4 - 6\frac{dy}{dx} = 0.$$

Simplify the result.

$$\frac{dy}{dx} = \frac{2x - 4}{6 - 2y} = \frac{x - 2}{3 - y}.$$

Substitute $x = -1$, $y = 7$ to find the gradient at $(-1, 7)$.

Substituting $x = -1$, $y = 7$ gives

$$\text{gradient} = \frac{-1 - 2}{3 - 7} = \frac{3}{4}.$$

6   Find the gradient at $\left(\frac{3}{2}, \frac{3}{2}\right)$ on the curve $x^3 + y^3 - 3xy = 0$.

$$x^3 + y^3 - 3xy = 0$$

Differentiate implicitly.

$$3x^2 + 3y^2\frac{dy}{dx} - 3x\frac{dy}{dx} - 3y = 0.$$

Simplify and substitute $x = y = \frac{3}{2}$.

$$\frac{dy}{dx} = \frac{y - x^2}{y^2 - x}.$$

At $\left(\frac{3}{2}, \frac{3}{2}\right)$, gradient is -1.

Differentiating implicitly and taking logarithms can sometimes lead to easier working for ordinary differentiating.

7   Differentiate $y = \sqrt{\dfrac{a - x}{a + x}}$.

Take logarithms, and simplify using logarithm rules.	$\ln y = \ln \sqrt{\left(\dfrac{a-x}{a+x}\right)}$
	$= \tfrac{1}{2}\ln(a-x) - \tfrac{1}{2}\ln(a+x).$
Differentiate implicitly.	$\dfrac{1}{y}\dfrac{dy}{dx} = \dfrac{-\tfrac{1}{2}}{a-x} - \dfrac{\tfrac{1}{2}}{a+x}.$
Simplify the right-hand side, multiply by y and simplify again.	$\dfrac{dy}{dx} = y\left(\dfrac{-\tfrac{1}{2}}{a-x} - \dfrac{\tfrac{1}{2}}{a+x}\right)$
	$= \tfrac{1}{2}y\left(\dfrac{-2a}{a^2-x^2}\right)$
	$= \left(\dfrac{a-x}{a+x}\right)\left(\dfrac{-a}{a^2-x^2}\right) = \dfrac{-a}{(a+x)^2}.$

Exercise 15

In questions 1 to 12, differentiate the following functions with respect to x.

1	$x+y$	**2**	$2x-y$
3	$2x^2 - 3y$	**4**	y^2
5	xy^2	**6**	$x^2 y^2$
7	$\dfrac{y}{x}$	**8**	$\dfrac{x}{y}$
9	$\sin y$	**10**	$\ln(xy)$
11	e^y	**12**	e^{y^2}

In questions 13 to 16, find $\dfrac{dy}{dx}$ in terms of x and y.

13 $x^2 + 2xy + 2y^2 = 5$ **14** $y^5 + 2xy^2 + x^5 = 4.$

15 $y + \ln y = 2x$ **16** $y^2 + xy^2 + x^2 = 3$

In questions 17 to 20, evaluate $\dfrac{dy}{dx}$ at the given point.

17 $16x^2 + 9y^2 = 52;\ (1,2)$ **18** $xy = 3;\ (-3,-1)$

19 $x^3 + 3x^2 y + 3xy^2 + 2y^3 = 2;\ (0,1)$ **20** $\cos\left(\pi\sqrt{xy}\right) = -\tfrac{1}{2};\ \left(\tfrac{1}{3}, \tfrac{4}{3}\right)$

16 Parametric differentiation

You will need to know

- that if $f(t)$ and $g(t)$ are functions of t, then $x = f(t)$ and $y = g(t)$ define a point on a curve for each value of t

- that the gradient $\dfrac{dy}{dx} = \dfrac{dy}{dt} \bigg/ \dfrac{dx}{dt}$, that is, $\dfrac{dy}{dx} = \dfrac{dy}{dt} \times \dfrac{dt}{dx}$, the composite function rule.

1 Let a curve be given parametrically by $x = t^2$, $y = 2t$. Find an expression for the gradient in terms of t.

$$x = t^2, \ y = 2t$$

Find $\dfrac{dx}{dt}$ and $\dfrac{dy}{dt}$.

$$\dfrac{dx}{dt} = 2t, \ \dfrac{dy}{dt} = 2.$$

Use $\dfrac{dy}{dx} = \dfrac{dy}{dt} \bigg/ \dfrac{dx}{dt}$ to find $\dfrac{dy}{dx}$.

$$\dfrac{dy}{dx} = \dfrac{2}{2t} = \dfrac{1}{t}.$$

2 Find the gradient at the point $t = \frac{1}{3}\pi$ for the curve $x = \sin t$, $y = 2\cos t$.

$$x = \sin t, \ y = 2\cos t$$

Find $\dfrac{dx}{dt}$ and $\dfrac{dy}{dt}$.

$$\dfrac{dx}{dt} = \cos t, \ \dfrac{dy}{dt} = -2\sin t.$$

Use $\dfrac{dy}{dx} = \dfrac{dy}{dt} \bigg/ \dfrac{dx}{dt}$ to find $\dfrac{dy}{dx}$.

$$\dfrac{dy}{dx} = \dfrac{-2\sin t}{\cos t} = -2\tan t.$$

Substitute $t = \frac{1}{3}\pi$ to find the gradient.

When $t = \frac{1}{3}\pi$,

gradient $= -2 \times \tan\frac{1}{3}\pi = -2\sqrt{3}$.

3   Find the equation of the normal at $t = 2$ on the curve $x = t^2$, $y = t^3$.

$$x = t^2, \ y = t^3.$$

Find $\dfrac{dx}{dt}$ and $\dfrac{dy}{dt}$.	$\dfrac{dx}{dt} = 2t, \ \dfrac{dy}{dt} = 3t^2.$
Use $\dfrac{dy}{dx} = \dfrac{dy}{dt} \bigg/ \dfrac{dx}{dt}$ to find $\dfrac{dy}{dx}$.	$\dfrac{dy}{dx} = \dfrac{3t^2}{2t} = \dfrac{3t}{2}.$

Substitute $t = 2$ to find the gradient of the tangent, and hence find the gradient of the normal.	When $t = 2$, gradient of tangent is $\dfrac{3 \times 2}{2} = 3$. So the gradient of the normal is $-\tfrac{1}{3}$.

Find the coordinates of the point on the curve for which $t = 2$.	When $t = 2$, $x = 2^2 = 4$ and $y = 2^3 = 8$.

Use $y - Y = m(x - X)$ to find the equation of the line through $(4, 8)$ with gradient $-\tfrac{1}{3}$.	The equation of the normal is $y - 8 = -\tfrac{1}{3}(x - 4)$, that is, $3y = -x + 28$.

4   Find a point on the curve whose parametric equation is $x = 2t + \sin 2t$, $y = 1 - \cos 2t$ for which the gradient is 1.

$$x = 2t + \sin 2t, \ y = 1 - \cos 2t$$

Find $\dfrac{dx}{dt}$ and $\dfrac{dy}{dt}$.	$\dfrac{dx}{dt} = 2 + 2\cos 2t, \ \dfrac{dy}{dt} = 2\sin 2t.$
Use $\dfrac{dy}{dx} = \dfrac{dy}{dt} \bigg/ \dfrac{dx}{dt}$ to find $\dfrac{dy}{dx}$.	$\dfrac{dy}{dx} = \dfrac{\sin 2t}{1 + \cos 2t}.$

Use the fact that the gradient is 1 to construct an equation.	If $\dfrac{dy}{dx} = 1$, then $\dfrac{\sin 2t}{1+\cos 2t} = 1$, so $\sin 2t - \cos 2t = 1$.
You need a trigonometric method to solve this equation completely, but you are only asked for one solution, which you can see by inspection.	There is a solution of this equation when $\sin 2t = 1$ and $\cos 2t = 0$, that is, when $2t = \frac{1}{2}\pi$. Thus there is a point on the curve when $t = \frac{1}{4}\pi$. The point is therefore $\left(\frac{1}{2}\pi + 1, 1\right)$.

Exercise 16

For each of the curves whose parametric equations are given in questions 1 to 10, find $\dfrac{dy}{dx}$ in terms of t.

1 $x = 2 + 3t, y = 12 - 6t$ **2** $x = 4 - 5t, y = 1 + t$

3 $x = t^2 - t, y = t^2 + t$ **4** $x = t^2 + 2t, y = 1 - t^2$

5 $x = e^t, y = 1 - t^2$ **6** $x = e^t + e^{-t}, y = e^t - e^{-t}$

7 $x = \cos^2 t, y = \sin^2 t$ **8** $x = \cos^3 t, y = \sin^3 t$

9 $x = \dfrac{t}{1+t^3}, y = \dfrac{t^2}{1+t^3}$ **10** $x = e^{2t} + 1, y = e^{2t} - 1$

In questions 11 to 16, find the gradient of the tangent to the curve at the given point.

11 $x = 2 - 3t, y = 1 + 2t, t = 2$ **12** $x = t^2, y = 1 + 2t, t = -3$

13 $x = \cos 2t, y = \cos^2 t, t = \frac{1}{6}\pi$ **14** $x = 2\cos 2t, y = 2\sin t, t = \frac{1}{6}\pi$.

15 $x = e^t, y = 1 - e^{-t}, t = 2$ **16** $x = \ln t, y = te^t, t = 2$

In questions 17 to 20, find the equation of the tangent to the curve at the given point.

17 $x = t^2, y = t, t = 2$ **18** $x = t, y = \dfrac{1}{t}, t = -3$

19 $x = t^3 + t^2, y = t^2 + t, t = -1$ **20** $x = \sin 2t, y = \sin t, t = -\frac{1}{3}\pi$

17 Related rates of change

You will need to know

- that if y and x are both functions of time t, then the rates of change $\dfrac{dy}{dt}$ and $\dfrac{dx}{dt}$ are related by the equation $\dfrac{dy}{dt} = \dfrac{dy}{dx} \times \dfrac{dx}{dt}$

- that the formula $\dfrac{dy}{dt} = \dfrac{dy}{dx} \times \dfrac{dx}{dt}$ is a form of the composite function rule.

1   A spherical balloon is being inflated. The radius is increasing at the rate of $0.2 \ \mathrm{cm\,s^{-1}}$. Find the rate at which the volume is increasing when the radius is 10 cm.

It is important to be organised. Decide what information you have, and what information you need to find.

Define the variables.	Let r cm be the radius and let $V \, \mathrm{cm}^3$ be the volume of the balloon at time t seconds.

You need to find the rate at which the volume is increasing, that is $\dfrac{dV}{dt}$. You are given that when $r = 10$, the rate of increase of r is 0.2, that is, $\dfrac{dr}{dt} = 0.2$. You also know that $\dfrac{dV}{dt}$ and $\dfrac{dr}{dt}$ are related by the formula $\dfrac{dV}{dt} = \dfrac{dV}{dr} \times \dfrac{dr}{dt}$, so if you can find $\dfrac{dV}{dr}$ you can start. But V is the volume of a spherical balloon of radius r so $V = \frac{4}{3}\pi r^3$; you can use this to find $\dfrac{dV}{dr}$.

Use the formula $\dfrac{dV}{dt} = \dfrac{dV}{dr} \times \dfrac{dr}{dt}$ with the given information.	For a sphere, $V = \frac{4}{3}\pi r^3$ so $\dfrac{dV}{dr} = 4\pi r^2$. Therefore $\dfrac{dV}{dt} = \dfrac{dV}{dr} \times \dfrac{dr}{dt}$ $\quad\quad\quad = 4\pi r^2 \times \dfrac{dr}{dt}$.
Substitute the known numerical values.	Also $\dfrac{dr}{dt} = 0.2$ when $r = 10$. Therefore $\dfrac{dV}{dt} = 4\pi r^2 \times \dfrac{dr}{dt}$ $\quad\quad\quad = 4\pi \times 10^2 \times 0.2$ $\quad\quad\quad = 80\pi$.
Present your answer.	The rate of increase of volume of the sphere is 80π cm^3 s^{-1}.

2   The side of a square is being increased at the rate of 0.3 cm s^{-1}. Find the rate at which the area of the square is increasing when the side of the square is 15 cm.

Define the variables.	Let x cm be the radius and let A cm^2 be the area of the square at time t seconds.
Use the formula $\dfrac{dA}{dt} = \dfrac{dA}{dx} \times \dfrac{dx}{dt}$ with the given information.	For a square, $A = x^2$ so $\dfrac{dA}{dx} = 2x$. Therefore $\dfrac{dA}{dt} = \dfrac{dA}{dx} \times \dfrac{dx}{dt}$ $\quad\quad\quad = 2x \times \dfrac{dx}{dt}$.

<table>
<tr><td>Substitute the known numerical values.</td><td>Also $\dfrac{dx}{dt} = 0.3$ when $x = 15$.

Therefore $\dfrac{dA}{dt} = 2x \times \dfrac{dx}{dt}$
$= 2 \times 15 \times 0.3$
$= 9.$</td></tr>
<tr><td>Present your answer.</td><td>The rate of increase of area of the square is $9\ \text{cm}^2\,\text{s}^{-1}$.</td></tr>
</table>

Sometimes you use the formula $\dfrac{dy}{dt} = \dfrac{dy}{dx} \times \dfrac{dx}{dt}$ in reverse to find $\dfrac{dx}{dt}$ knowing $\dfrac{dy}{dt}$.

3 The area of a square is increasing at the rate of $48\ \text{cm}^2\,\text{s}^{-1}$. Find the rate at which the side of the square is increasing when the side of the square is 12 cm.

<table>
<tr><td>Define the variables.</td><td>Let x cm be the radius and let A cm^2 be the area of the square at t seconds.</td></tr>
<tr><td>Use the formula $\dfrac{dA}{dt} = \dfrac{dA}{dx} \times \dfrac{dx}{dt}$ with the given information.</td><td>For a square, $A = x^2$ so $\dfrac{dA}{dx} = 2x$.

Therefore $\dfrac{dA}{dt} = \dfrac{dA}{dx} \times \dfrac{dx}{dt}$
$= 2x \times \dfrac{dx}{dt}$.</td></tr>
<tr><td>Substitute the known numerical values.</td><td>From $\dfrac{dA}{dt} = 2x \times \dfrac{dx}{dt}$
$48 = 2 \times 12 \times \dfrac{dx}{dt}$
so $\dfrac{dx}{dt} = \dfrac{48}{2 \times 12} = 2.$</td></tr>
<tr><td>Present your answer.</td><td>The rate of increase of the side of the square is $2\ \text{cm}\,\text{s}^{-1}$.</td></tr>
</table>

Exercise 17

Where appropriate, leave π in your answers.

1   A spherical balloon is being inflated. When the radius is 4 cm the rate of increase of the radius is 0.5 cm s^{-1}. Find the rate at which the surface area of the sphere is increasing at that moment.

2   The radius of a circle is increasing at the rate of 3 cm s^{-1}. Find the rate of increase of the perimeter when the radius is 5 cm.

3   The radius of a circle is increasing at the rate of 4 cm s^{-1}. Find the rate of increase of the area when the radius is 2 cm.

4   When the volume of a cubical box is 216 cm^3 the side is increasing at the rate of 2 cm s^{-1}. Find the rate of increase of the volume of the box, and the rate of increase of the surface area at that time.

5   The area of a circle is increasing at the rate of 20 cm^2 s^{-1}. Find the rate of increase of the radius when the radius is 4 cm.

6   Liquid is being poured at a constant rate of 20 cm^3 s^{-1} into a vessel in the shape of a right circular cone with its axis vertical and its vertex downwards. The semi-vertical angle of the cone is $\tan^{-1}\frac{1}{2}$. Find the rate of increase of the height when the radius of the surface is 2 cm.

7   The height of a particular circular cylinder is always twice its radius. The volume of the cylinder is increasing at the constant rate 40π cm^3 s^{-1}. Find the rate of increase of the radius when the radius is 5 cm.

8   When the area of a square is 100 cm^2, the rate of change of area is 8 cm^2 s^{-1}. Find the rate of change of the perimeter at that time.

9   The surface area of a cube is increasing at a rate of 12 cm^2 s^{-1}. Find the rate at which the volume is increasing when the surface area is 150 cm^2.

10   Find the rate of increase of surface area of a sphere when its volume is 36π cm^3 and the volume is increasing at the rate 24π cm^3 s^{-1}.

18 Small increases

You will need to know

- the relation $\delta y \approx \dfrac{dy}{dx}\,\delta x$, and the meanings of the various terms in it

- the equivalent relation in function notation, $f(x+h) \approx f(x) + hf'(x)$.

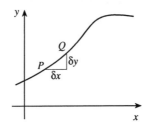

Fig. 18.1

In Fig. 18.1, δy is the increase in the value of the function from its value at the known point P if you increase the x-coordinate by δx. You can see that, if δx is small, then the gradient of the chord joining P to Q is approximately the same as the tangent at P, so that $\dfrac{\delta y}{\delta x} \approx \dfrac{dy}{dx}$. The relationship $\delta y \approx \dfrac{dy}{dx}\,\delta x$ follows immediately.

Alternatively, in Fig. 18.2, the same geometrical relationship is expressed by saying that the increase corresponding to δy is $f(x+h) - f(x)$, and δx is replaced by h.

Then $\dfrac{f(x+h) - f(x)}{h} \approx f'(x)$, leading to $f(x+h) \approx f(x) + hf'(x)$.

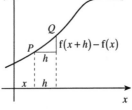

Fig. 18.2

Examples will be worked in both notations: choose whichever one you prefer, but you should understand that the two notations are mathematically equivalent.

1 Use calculus to show that the increase in the function $y = x^3$ as x increases from 2 to 2.01 is approximately 0.12.

$$y = x^3$$

Find $\dfrac{dy}{dx}$.

$$\dfrac{dy}{dx} = 3x^2.$$

The value of x is 2, and $x + \delta x = 2.01$. The value of δx is therefore 0.01. Use $\delta y \approx \dfrac{dy}{dx} \delta x$ to find the increase in y.

Then $\delta y \approx \dfrac{dy}{dx} \delta x = 3x^2 \delta x.$

Substitute the values of x and δx.

$$\delta y \approx 3x^2 \delta x$$
$$= 3 \times 2^2 \times 0.01 = 0.12.$$

Present the result.

The approximate increase in the function is 0.12.

2 Start from the value of $\cos \frac{1}{3}\pi$ to find an approximation to the value of $\cos 1$.

Define a function.

Let $f(x) = \cos x$.

Define x and $x + h$ to find the value of h.

Let $x = \frac{1}{3}\pi$ and $x + h = 1$.
Then $h = 1 - \frac{1}{3}\pi = -0.047\ldots$.

Use $f(x + h) \approx f(x) + hf'(x)$

$$f(1) \approx f\left(\tfrac{1}{3}\pi\right) + (-0.047\ldots) \times f'\left(\tfrac{1}{3}\pi\right)$$
$$= 0.5 - 0.047\ldots \times -\sin\left(\tfrac{1}{3}\pi\right)$$
$$= 0.5408\ldots.$$

You can compare this with the true value for $\cos 1$ *which is* $0.5403....$

3   Use the fact that $6.4^2 = 40.96$ to find an approximation to $\sqrt{41}$, without using a calculator.

Define a function.	Let $y = \sqrt{x} = x^{\frac{1}{2}}$.

Prepare to use the formula $\delta y \approx \dfrac{\mathrm{d}y}{\mathrm{d}x}\,\delta x$ *by finding all the constituent parts.*

Calculate $\dfrac{\mathrm{d}y}{\mathrm{d}x}$ and define δx.	Let $x = 40.96$. Since $x + \delta x = 41$, $\delta x = (x + \delta x) - x = 41 - 40.96 = 0.04$. $\dfrac{\mathrm{d}y}{\mathrm{d}x} = \tfrac{1}{2} x^{-\frac{1}{2}} = \dfrac{1}{2\sqrt{x}}$. When $x = 40.96$, $\dfrac{\mathrm{d}y}{\mathrm{d}x} = \dfrac{1}{2 \times 6.4}$.
Use $\delta y \approx \dfrac{\mathrm{d}y}{\mathrm{d}x}\,\delta x$.	$\delta y \approx \dfrac{\mathrm{d}y}{\mathrm{d}x}\,\delta x = \dfrac{1}{2 \times 6.4} \times 0.04$ $= 0.003125.$
Present the result $y + \delta y$.	$\sqrt{41} \approx 6.4 + 0.003125 = 6.403125.$

You can compare this with the true value for $\sqrt{41}$ *which is* $6.403124....$

4   Find the approximate value of $\dfrac{1}{3.02}$.

Define a function.	Let $\mathrm{f}(x) = x^{-1}$.
Calculate $\mathrm{f}'(x)$ and define x and h.	Let $x = 3$ and $h = 0.02$. $\mathrm{f}'(x) = -x^{-2}$.

Use $f(x+h) \approx f(x) + hf'(x)$.

$$f(x+h) \approx \frac{1}{3} + 0.02 \times \left(-\frac{1}{9}\right)$$
$$= 0.33111\ldots.$$

Exercise 18

In questions 1 to 4 use calculus to find the approximate increase in the following functions as x increases from 1 to 1.05.

1 $y = 2x^3$ **2** $y = x^2 - 3x$

3 $y = (x-1)^3$ **4** $y = \cos\frac{1}{3}\pi x$

In questions 5 to 8 use calculus to approximate to the value of the given function at $x = -0.99$.

5 $f(x) = 3x^2$ **6** $f(x) = \sqrt{2+x}$

7 $f(x) = \dfrac{x}{x-1}$ **8** $f(x) = \dfrac{x^2}{x^2+1}$

In questions 9 to 12, use calculus to calculate an approximation to the given quantity by choosing suitable functions and increases.

9 $\sqrt{26}$ **10** $(65)^{\frac{1}{3}}$

11 $\dfrac{1}{24}$ **12** 99^2

19 Curve sketching

You will need to know

- the shapes of the graphs of the trigonometric, exponential and logarithmic functions

- the shapes of the graphs of powers of x

- how to find the coordinates of local maxima and minima

- what an asymptote is

- that vertical asymptotes occur when the denominator of a fraction is zero

- that for expressions such as xe^{-x} when x becomes large, and $x\ln x$ when x becomes small, the exponential function is always 'more powerful' than a power of x, and a power of x is always 'more powerful' than the logarithmic function, that is, $xe^{-x} \to 0$ for large x, and $x\ln x \to 0$ for x positive and close to 0.

To sketch the graph of a function you need to give an idea of its general shape, together with the coordinates of special points, including those where the graph crosses the axes, and any maxima or minima. Remember that a sketch of a graph does not need to be drawn to scale with graduations along the axes.

1   Sketch the graph of $y = \dfrac{x-1}{x+1}$.

First find where the curve crosses the x- and y-axes.	When $x = 0$, $y = -1$ and when $y = 0$, $x = 1$, so $(0, -1)$ and $(1, 0)$ lie on the curve.
Find any vertical asymptotes, by looking for places where the denominator is 0.	The denominator is 0 when $x = -1$, so there is a vertical asymptote when $x = -1$.

You need to find what happens as $x \to \infty$ and $x \to -\infty$. Many people do this by mentally substituting a large number, say one million, and seeing what happens to the value of the function.

Sketch the graph of $y = \dfrac{x-1}{x+1}$ (continued).

Find what happens as $x \to \infty$ and as $x \to -\infty$?	As $x \to \infty$, $y \to 1$ from below. As $x \to -\infty$, $y \to 1$ from above.

You need also to find out how the graph behaves just to the left and to the right of the vertical asymptote. You can do this by mentally substituting numbers. In this case, you might substitute $x = -1.01$ to find how y behaves to the left of the asymptote, and $x = -0.99$ for the behaviour to the right of the asymptote.

Find what happens as $x = -1$ from above and below.	For x just less than -1, y is large and positive. For x just greater than -1, y is large and negative.
Find any local maxima and minima.	$\dfrac{dy}{dx} = \dfrac{(x+1)1 - (x-1)1}{(x+1)^2} = \dfrac{2}{(x+1)^2}.$ 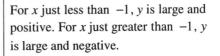 $\dfrac{dy}{dx} \neq 0$ for any value of x so there are no local maxima and minima.
You now have enough evidence to sketch the graph.	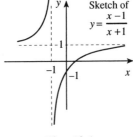

Fig. 19.1

2 Sketch the graph of $y = \dfrac{x}{x^2 + 1}$.

First find where the curve crosses the x- and y-axes.	When $x = 0$, $y = 0$.

Find any vertical asymptotes, by looking for places where the denominator is 0.	As $x^2 + 1 \neq 0$ for any x, there are no vertical asymptotes.
Find what happens as $x \to \infty$ and as $x \to -\infty$?	As $x \to \infty$, $y \to 0$ from above. As $x \to -\infty$, $y \to 0$ from below.
Find any local maxima and minima and identify them.	$\dfrac{dy}{dx} = \dfrac{(x^2+1)1 - x \times 2x}{(x^2+1)^2} = \dfrac{1-x^2}{(x^2+1)^2}$. $\dfrac{dy}{dx} = 0$ when $x = \pm 1$. $\dfrac{d^2y}{dx^2} = \dfrac{2x(x^2-3)}{(x^2+1)^3}$. When $x = 1$, $\dfrac{d^2y}{dx^2} < 0$ so $\left(1, \tfrac{1}{2}\right)$ is a local maximum; when $x = -1$, $\dfrac{d^2y}{dx^2} > 0$ so $\left(-1, -\tfrac{1}{2}\right)$ is a local minimum.
You now have enough evidence to sketch the graph.	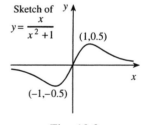 Sketch of $y = \dfrac{x}{x^2+1}$ (1, 0.5) (−1, −0.5)

Fig. 19.2

3   Sketch the graph of $y = xe^{-x}$.

First find where the curve crosses the x- and y-axes.	When $x = 0$, $y = 0$.

Sketch the graph of $y = xe^{-x}$ (continued).

Find any vertical asymptotes, by looking for places where the denominator is 0.	There are no vertical asymptotes.
Find what happens as $x \to \infty$ and as $x \to -\infty$?	As $x \to \infty$, $x \to \infty$ and $e^{-x} \to 0$, but e^{-x} is more powerful that x, so $xe^{-x} \to 0$. As $x \to -\infty$, $xe^{-x} \to -\infty$ from below.
Find any local maxima and minima and identify them.	$\dfrac{dy}{dx} = x\left(-e^{-x}\right) + e^{-x} \times 1 = e^{-x}(1-x)$. $\dfrac{dy}{dx} = 0$ when $x = 1$. (Remember $e^{-x} \neq 0$ for any x.) $\dfrac{d^2y}{dx^2} = e^{-x}(x-2)$. When $x = 1$, $\dfrac{d^2y}{dx^2} < 0$ so $\left(1, e^{-1}\right)$ is a local maximum.
You now have enough evidence to sketch the graph.	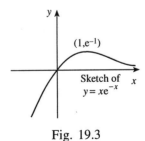

Fig. 19.3

4   Sketch the graph of $y = x \sin x$.

First find where the curve crosses the *x*- and *y*-axes.

When $x = 0$, $y = 0$. When $y = 0$, $x \sin x = 0$, so $x = n\pi$, n an integer.

Find any vertical asymptotes, by looking for places where the denominator is 0.

There are no vertical asymptotes.

Find what happens as $x \to \infty$ and as $x \to -\infty$?

As $x \to \infty$ and $x \to -\infty$, the curve oscillates between $y = x$ and $y = -x$.

Find any local maxima and minima and identify them.

$\dfrac{dy}{dx} = x \cos x + \sin x$. $\dfrac{dy}{dx} = 0$ when $x \cos x + \sin x = 0$ or $\tan x = -x$. This equation cannot be solved analytically, but if you consider the equations $y = -x$ and $y = \tan x$ you can see that there are solutions in every interval of π on the *x*-axis.

You now have enough evidence to sketch the graph.

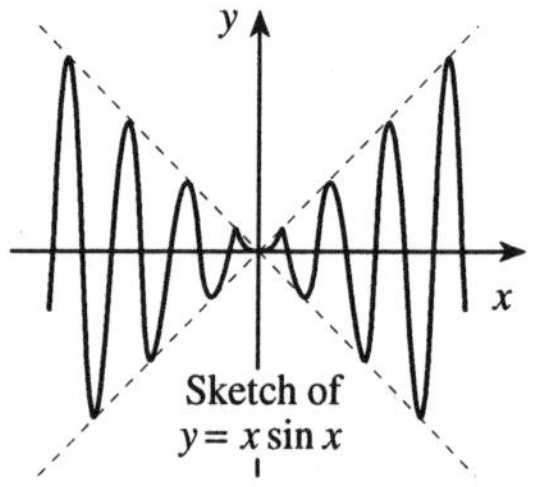

Sketch of
$y = x \sin x$

Fig. 19.4

Sometimes there are graphs which do not appear to have many of the above qualities. In that case you must do what you can.

5   Sketch the graph of $y = \sqrt{x^2 - 1}$.

Remember that the square root function is always positive. There are no points on the graph of this function for which y is negative.

First find where the curve crosses the *x*- and *y*-axes.	When $x = 0$, $y = \sqrt{-1}$. Therefore the curve does not cross the *y*-axis. When $y = 0$, $\sqrt{x^2 - 1} = 0$, so $x = \pm 1$
Find any vertical asymptotes, by looking for places where the denominator is 0.	There are no vertical asymptotes.
Find what happens as $x \to \infty$ and as $x \to -\infty$?	As $x \to \infty$, the curve becomes close to, but slightly less than $y = x$. For $x \to -\infty$, becomes close to, but slightly less than $y = -x$.
Find any local maxima and minima and identify them.	$\dfrac{dy}{dx} = \dfrac{x}{\sqrt{x^2 - 1}}$. $\dfrac{dy}{dx} = 0$ when $x = 0$, but there are no points on the graph for $x = 0$. Therefore there are no local maxima or minima.
You now have enough evidence to sketch the graph.	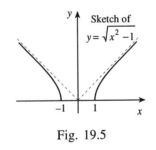

Fig. 19.5

6   Sketch the graph of $y = x \ln x$.

Remember that $\ln x$ *is defined only for positive values of x.*

First find where the curve crosses the *x*- and *y*-axes.

When $x = 0$, $\ln x$ is not defined so there is no point for which $x = 0$. When $y = 0$, $x \ln x = 0$, so $x = 0$ or $\ln x = 0$. As $x = 0$ is impossible, this leaves $\ln x = 0$, that is $x = 1$.

Find any vertical asymptotes, by looking for places where the denominator is 0.

There are no vertical asymptotes.

Find what happens as $x \to \infty$ and as $x \to -\infty$?

As $x \to \infty$, the curve becomes very large. As $x \to 0$, $\ln x \to -\infty$ and $x \to 0$, but "x wins" in the product $x \ln x$ so $x \ln x \to 0$

Find any local maxima and minima and identify them.

$\dfrac{dy}{dx} = x \times \dfrac{1}{x} + \ln x = \ln x + 1$. $\dfrac{dy}{dx} = 0$

when $\ln x = -1$, giving $x = e^{-1}$.

$\dfrac{d^2 y}{dx^2} = \dfrac{1}{x}$, which is positive when

$x = e^{-1}$. Hence $\left(e^{-1}, -e^{-1} \right)$ is a local minimum.

You now have enough evidence to sketch the graph.

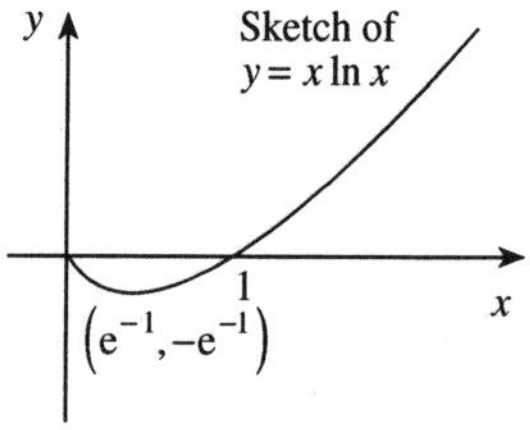

Fig. 19.6

Exercise 19

In questions 1 to 16 sketch the graphs of the following functions.

1 $y = 1 - \dfrac{1}{x+2}$ **2** $y = \dfrac{x+1}{x-1}$

3 $y = \dfrac{x^2 - 1}{x^2 + 1}$ **4** $y = \dfrac{x}{x^2 - 1}$

5 $y = x^2 e^{-x}$ **6** $y = e^x - x$

7 $y = x + \dfrac{1}{x}$ **8** $y = x^2 + \dfrac{1}{x^2}$

9 $y = \sqrt{x^2 + 1}$ **10** $y = \sqrt{x^2}$

11 $y = x - \ln x$ **12** $y = \dfrac{x^2}{\ln x}$

13 $y = e^{-x} \cos x$ **14** $y = x \cos x$

15 $y = \dfrac{e^{-x}}{x^2}$ **16** $y = \ln(-x)$

20 Revision exercises

Revision exercise 1

1 Differentiate $2\sqrt{x}$, and find its value when $x = 4$.

2 Find the equation of the normal to the curve $y = x^2$ at the point $(3,9)$ and find the x-coordinate of the point where this normal meets the curve again.

3 An oscillating particle is moving in a straight line so that its displacement x metres after t seconds is given by $x = 3\sin t$. Find the velocity and acceleration of the particle after 2 seconds.

4 Find the local maxima and minima, and the point of inflexion of the curve $y = x^3 - 3x^2 - 24x$.

5 Differentiate $y = \dfrac{\sqrt{x^2 + 1}}{x + 1}$ with respect to x.

6 Sketch the graph of $y = x^2 - 2x - 3$.

Revision exercise 2

1 Find the gradient of the curve $y = \dfrac{1}{\sqrt{x}}$ when $x = 9$.

2 Find the equation of the tangent at the point $t = 2$ to the curve $x = 1 - t$, $y = 1 + t^2$.

3 The amount A grams of a radioactive substance present varies with time t seconds according to the law $A = A_0 e^{-kt}$, where A_0 and k are constants. Find how much of the substance exists at the start of the process, and find the rate of decrease of the substance when the amount is one half of the starting value.

4 The top and bottom margins of a page are each 1 cm, and the left and right margins are each 1.5 cm. The area of the print on each page is 150 cm^2. Find the dimensions of the page which has the least area.

5 Find the gradient of the curve $x^2 + xy + y^2 = 4$ at the point $(-2, 2)$.

6 Differentiate $x^2 \sin(x^2 + 1)$.

Revision exercise 3

1 Find the points on the graph of $y = \dfrac{x}{x^2+1}$ at which the gradient is $\frac{12}{25}$.

2 The liquid in a container is draining through a hole in the bottom so that, between $t = 0$ and $t = 4$ minutes, the height in centimetres of the surface of the liquid above the base is given by $h = \frac{1}{4}(4-t)^2$. Find the rate at which the surface is falling when the height is 2 cm.

3 Find the points of inflexion on the graph of $y = \sin x$.

4 The height y in metres of a ball thrown vertically into the air is given by $y = 10t - 5t^2$ where t seconds is the time after which it was thrown. Find the velocity of the ball when it is at height $3\frac{3}{4}$ metres.

5 Find the maximum and minimum values of $x^2 e^{-x}$.

6 Sketch the graph of $y = 3 + 3x - 4x^2 - x^3$.

Revision exercise 4

1 Differentiate $xy^2 = y^3 + 1$ implicitly to find $\dfrac{dy}{dx}$ in terms of x and y.

2 Find the equation of the normal at the point $t = -1$ to the curve $x = t^2$, $y = 2t$.

3 Find the maxima, minima and points of inflexion of the curve $y = \frac{1}{2}\left(e^x + e^{-x}\right)$.

4 Find the shortest line segment which passes through $(8, 27)$, and has one end on the x-axis and the other on the y-axis.

5 Use a calculus method to find the approximate increase in volume of a sphere of radius 2 metres, when the radius is increased by 1 cm.

6 Find a point on the graph of $y = 2\sin x - 3\cos x$ at which the gradient is the same as that of the straight line $y = x$.

Revision exercise 5

1 Sketch the graph of the function $y = (x-1)\sqrt{x}$.

2 A curve is given parametrically by $x = \cos t$, $y = \sin^2 t$. Find the smallest positive value of t such that the angle that the tangent to the curve makes with the x-axis is $60°$.

3 Differentiate $2x^2 \ln x$ with respect to x.

4 Find the maximum and minimum values of the function
   $f(x) = \sin 3x - 3\sin x$.

5 Differentiate the equation $\sqrt{x} + \sqrt{y} = \sqrt{a}$ to find an expression for $\dfrac{dy}{dx}$.

6 Find a condition on a and b such that if the condition holds, then the graph of $y = x^3 + ax^2 + bx + c$ has a local maximum and a local minimum.

Revision exercise 6

1 The length of a rectangle is twice its width. Find the rate at which the area is increasing when the perimeter is 30 cm and increasing at the rate of 5 cm s^{-1}.

2 Differentiate $\dfrac{4x + 2}{\sqrt{x}}$ with respect to x.

3 Find the local maxima and minima on the curve $y = \left(x^2 - 1\right)^2$.

4 Find $\dfrac{dy}{dx}$ in terms of x and y when $2x^2 - 3xy + 4y^2 = 3$.

5 Find the equation of the normal at the point with parameter $\tfrac{1}{4}\pi$ to the curve $x = 2\sin t$, $y = \cos t$.

6 Find the x-coordinates of the points of inflexion on the curve $y = x^4 - 3x^2 + 2$.

21 Answers

Exercise 2, page 7

1 For Fig. 2.7, the maximum gradient is 4 and the minimum is –3. The gradient graph is shown in Fig. 21.1.

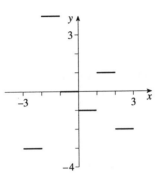

Fig. 21.1

2 For Fig. 2.8, the maximum gradient is 4 and the minimum is –4. The gradient graph is shown in Fig. 21.2.

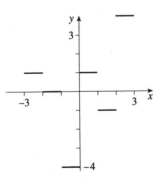

Fig. 21.2

3 For Fig. 2.9, the gradient is positive for $-3 < x < 1$ and negative for $1 < x < 3$. The gradient graph is shown in Fig. 21.3.

Fig. 21.3

4 For Fig. 2.10, the gradient is positive for $-2 < x < 1$ and negative for $-3 < x < -2$ and $1 < x < 3$. The gradient graph is shown in Fig. 21.4.

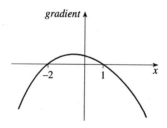

Fig. 21.4

Exercise 3, page 12

1	$14x$	**2**	$15x^2$
3	a	**4**	$2bx$
5	$3cx^2$	**6**	$2x + 4$
7	$6x - 5$	**8**	$3x^2 + 2x$
9	$4x^3$	**10**	$24x^3$
11	$6x^2 - 6x$	**12**	$5x^4$
13	$6x - 7$	**14**	$6 - 14x$
15	$3x^2 - 10x + 3$	**16**	$6x^2 - 8x + 1$
17	$-2x^{-3}$	**18**	$-2x^{-2}$
19	$-6x^{-4} - x^{-3}$	**20**	$-x^{-4} + x$
21	0	**22**	$8 - 8x^{-3}$
23	$3 + 9x^{-4}$	**24**	$x^{-\frac{1}{2}}$
25	$-2x^{-\frac{5}{3}}$	**26**	$x^{-\frac{2}{3}} - 4x^{-3} + 1$

27 $2 + 6x^{-4}$

28 $6x^{\frac{1}{2}} + x^{-\frac{3}{2}} + 3$

29 $\dfrac{-2}{x^3}$

30 $-\dfrac{1}{\sqrt{x}} - 3$

31 $-\dfrac{1}{2x^{\frac{3}{2}}}$

32 $\frac{3}{2}\sqrt{x}$

33 $2x + 6$

34 $8x$

35 $2x - \dfrac{2}{x^3}$

36 $1 - \dfrac{1}{x^2}$

37 $-\dfrac{1}{x^2}$

38 $-\dfrac{2}{x^2} - \dfrac{2}{x^3}$

39 $3x^2$

40 $2x - \dfrac{1}{x^2}$

41 $8x$

42 $\dfrac{\sqrt{3}}{2\sqrt{x}}$

43 $\dfrac{1}{\sqrt{x}}$

44 $\dfrac{\sqrt[3]{3}}{3\sqrt[3]{x^2}}$

45 $(1,6), 5$

46 $(2,9), 9$

47 $(0,0), 2$

48 $(-2,6), -5$

49 $(3,6), 11$

50 $(4,2), \frac{1}{4}$

51 $(1,2)$

52 $(-1,1)$

53 $\left(\frac{1}{2}, 2\right), \left(-\frac{1}{2}, -2\right)$

54 $(16,64)$

55 $(1,-3)$

56 $(2,-1), \left(-\frac{2}{3}, 4\frac{17}{27}\right)$

Exercise 4, page 19

1 $y = -2x - 1$

2 $y = -3x + 4$

3 $3y = x + 9$

4 $y = 2x - 2$

5 $4y + x = 4$

6 $y = 4x - 4$

7 $2y = x + 3$

8 $3y = x + 12$

9 $y = -3x + 33$

10 $2y = -x + 1$

11 $2y = 8x - 15$

12 $4y = -x + 1$

13 $y = 9x - 27; 9y = -x + 3$

14 $y = x - 1; y = -x - 1$

15 $y = 0; y = -4$

16 $y = 2ax - a^2; 2ay = -x + 2a^3 + a$

17 $y = 2x + 2; (2,6)$

18 $(0,0)$

19 $y = (2a+1)x + 1 - a^2; (1,3), (-1,1)$

Exercise 5, page 26

1 1st and 5th seconds; the toy is at rest; -50 cm s^{-1}
2 At times 1.5 s and 4.5 s; at 0.75 s, 2.25 s, 3.75 s and 5.25 s.
3 2 m s^{-1}
4 $(5-2t)$ m s^{-1}, 2.5 s
5 $(6-2t)$ m s^{-1}, -2 m s^{-2}, 2 s
6 4 m s^{-2}, 10 m s^{-2}
7 5 m
8 $v = 3t^2 - 18t + 24$, $a = 6t - 18$, 8 m, 4 m, 6 m
9 (a) 320 °C, 60 °C min^{-1} (b) 30 °C min^{-1}, 0 °C min^{-1}. The hot plate is not losing heat any more. Note that the quadratic function does not describe the temperature well after 10 minutes.

Exercise 6, page 34

1 Minimum at $(3,-6)$
2 Maximum at $(-2,11)$
3 Maximum at $(3,9)$
4 Minimum at $\left(-1\frac{1}{2}, 2\frac{1}{4}\right)$
5 Minimum at $(0,0)$, maximum at $\left(1\frac{1}{3}, 1\frac{5}{27}\right)$
6 Minimum at $(1,-3)$, maximum at $(-1,1)$
7 Minimum at $\left(-\frac{1}{3}, -5\frac{1}{3}\right)$
8 Maximum at $(-2,16)$
9 Maximum at $\left(1\frac{1}{4}, 3\frac{1}{8}\right)$
10 Minimum at $(2,-14)$, maximum at $(-2,18)$
11 Maximum at $(1,1)$, minimum at $(2,0)$
12 Maximum at $(3,28)$, minimum at $(-1,-4)$
13 Horizontal point of inflexion at $(-1,2)$
14 Horizontal point of inflexion at $(2,-3)$
15 Minimum at $(1,4)$, maximum at $(-1,0)$
16 Minimum at $(3,-75)$, maximum at $(-2,50)$
17 Maximum at $(1,13)$, minimum at $(-2,-14)$
18 Horizontal point of inflexion at $(0,3)$
19 Minimum at $(2,-38)$, maximum at $(-3,87)$
20 Horizontal point of inflexion at $(0,2)$
21 Minimum at $(1,3)$

2 2 Minimum at $(2,11)$, maximum at $(-2,-5)$

2 3 Maximum at $(1,0)$, minimum at $\left(2\frac{1}{3},-1\frac{5}{27}\right)$

2 4 Horizontal point of inflexion at $(3,2)$

2 5 Minimum at $(-2,12)$

Exercise 7, page 39

1 Maximum at $\left(1\frac{1}{4},3\frac{1}{8}\right)$

2 Minimum at $(2,-14)$, maximum at $(-2,18)$

3 Maximum at $(1,1)$, minimum at $(2,0)$

4 Maximum at $(3,28)$, minimum at $(-1,-4)$

5 Horizontal point of inflexion at $(-1,2)$

6 Horizontal point of inflexion at $(2,-3)$

7 Horizontal point of inflexion at $(3,2)$

8 Minimum at $(3,-75)$, maximum at $(-2,50)$

9 Maximum at $(1,13)$, minimum at $(-2,-14)$

1 0 Horizontal point of inflexion at $(0,3)$

1 1 Minimum at $(2,-38)$, maximum at $(-3,87)$

1 2 Horizontal point of inflexion at $(0,2)$

1 3 Minimum at $(1,3)$

1 4 Minimum at $(2,11)$, maximum at $(-2,-5)$

1 5 Minimum at $(1,4)$, maximum at $(-1,0)$

1 6 Minimum at $(-2,12)$

Exercise 8, page 46

In the answers to this exercise, to save space the type (see Fig. 8.2 on page 40) of quadratic or cubic is given, together with the intercepts of the curve with the axes and the maxima, minima and horizontal points of inflexion, in order.

1 Quadratic, Type A, $(0,3)$, minimum at $(3,-6)$

2 Quadratic, Type B, $(0,7)$, maximum at $(-2,11)$

3 Quadratic, Type B, $(0,0)$, $(6,0)$, maximum at $(3,9)$

4 Quadratic, Type A, $(0,0)$, $(-3,0)$, minimum at $\left(-1\frac{1}{2},2\frac{1}{4}\right)$

5 Cubic, Type D, $(0,0)$, $(2,0)$, minimum at $(0,0)$, maximum at $\left(1\frac{1}{3},1\frac{5}{27}\right)$

6 Cubic, Type A, $(0,-1)$, minimum at $(1,-3)$, maximum at $(-1,1)$

7 Quadratic, Type A, $(0,-5)$, $(1,0)$, $\left(-1\frac{2}{3},0\right)$, minimum at $\left(-\frac{1}{3},-5\frac{1}{3}\right)$

8 Quadratic, Type B, $(0,4)$, maximum at $(-2,16)$

9 Quadratic, Type B, $(0,0)$, $\left(2\frac{1}{2},0\right)$, maximum at $\left(1\frac{1}{4},3\frac{1}{8}\right)$

1 0 Cubic, Type A, $(0,2)$, minimum at $(2,-14)$, maximum at $(-2,18)$

11 Cubic, Type A, $(0,-4)$, $\left(\frac{1}{2},0\right)$, minimum at $(2,0)$, maximum at $(1,1)$

12 Cubic, Type D, $(0,1)$, minimum at $(-1,-4)$, maximum at $(3,28)$

13 Cubic, Type E, $(0,1)$, horizontal point of inflexion at $(-1,2)$

14 Cubic, Type B, $(0,-11)$, horizontal point of inflexion at $(2,-3)$

15 Cubic, Type E, $(0,29)$, horizontal point of inflexion at $(3,2)$

16 Cubic, Type A, $(0,6)$, minimum at $(3,-75)$, maximum at $(-2,50)$

17 Cubic, Type D, $(0,6)$, maximum at $(1,13)$, minimum at $(-2,-14)$

18 Cubic, Type E, $(0,3)$, horizontal point of inflexion at $(0,3)$

19 Cubic, Type A, $(0,6)$, minimum at $(2,-38)$, maximum at $(-3,87)$

20 Cubic, Type B, $(0,2)$, horizontal point of inflexion at $(0,2)$

21 Cubic, Type A, $(0,-3)$, $(1,0)$, $(3,0)$, maximum $(1,0)$, minimum $\left(2\frac{1}{3},-1\frac{5}{27}\right)$

22 Cubic, Type F, $(0,3)$

Exercise 9, page 50

1	$x=-1$	2	$x=2$
3	$x=-1,4$	4	$x=0,1$
5	None	6	None

Exercise 10, page 55

1	$7\frac{11}{27}\,\text{cm}^3$	2	$18\,\text{cm}^3$
3	27	4	24
5	$64\,\text{m}^2$	6	A 3 cm cube
7	$48\,\text{m}^2$	8	490 m
9	$3\frac{1}{3}$	10	20 cm
11	$1024\,\text{cm}^3$	12	20
13	$891\,\text{m}^2$	14	A 6 cm cube
15	$48\,\text{cm}^3$	16	$x=y=24$
17	$12\,\text{cm}\times12\,\text{cm}\times13\,\text{cm}$	18	$\left(800/(3\pi+8)\right)\text{m}$
19	$3\left(2\pi V^2\right)^{\frac{1}{3}}$	20	$(360/\pi)^\circ$

Exercise 11, page 62

1	$4(2x+1)$	2	$-9(1-3x)^2$
3	$(2x+5)^{-\frac{1}{2}}$	4	$-4(4x-1)^{-2}$
5	$2(x-3)$	6	$\frac{3}{2}(3x+2)^{-\frac{1}{2}}$

7 $12x(2x^2+3)^2$ **8** $3x(x^2+2)^{\frac{1}{2}}$

9 $x(x^2+2)^{-\frac{1}{2}}$ **10** $16x(x^2+2)^7$

11 $\frac{1}{2}(x+1)^{-\frac{1}{2}}$ **12** $20(3x-1)(3x^2-2x)^9$

13 $-4(2x-1)^{-3}$ **14** $2(1-2x)^{-2}$

15 $\frac{1}{2}b(a+bx)^{-\frac{1}{2}}$ **16** $-2x(a^2+x^2)^{-2}$

Exercise 12, page 68

1 $(2x+3)\times 3+2\times(3x+4);\ 12x+17$

2 $(x^2-1)\times 2+2x\times(2x+1);\ 6x^2+2x-2$

3 $(x^2-3x+2)\times\frac{1}{2}+(2x-3)\times(\frac{1}{2}x+1);\ 1\frac{1}{2}x^2-x-2$

4 $(x^3-1)\times 3x^2+3x^2\times(x^3+1);\ 6x^5$

5 $(2x-3)\times 4x+2\times(2x^2-5);\ 12x^2-12x-10$

6 $(x-1)\times(3x^2+2x+1)+1\times(x^3+x^2+x+1);\ 4x^3$

7 $(x^2+2x)\times(4x-3)+(2x+2)\times(2x^2-3x);\ x(8x^2+3x-12)$

8 $(x+1)\times\frac{1}{2}x^{-\frac{1}{2}}+1\times x^{\frac{1}{2}};\ \dfrac{3x+1}{2x^{\frac{1}{2}}}$

9 $(x+2)\times(2x-2)+1\times(x^2-2x+4);\ 3x^2$

10 $(x-3)\times(2x+3)+1\times(x^2+3x+9);\ 3x^2$

11 $(x+1)(x^2+1)\times 3x^2+(x+1)\times 2x\times(x^3+1)+1\times(x^2+1)(x^3+1);$

     $6x^5+5x^4+4x^3+3x^2+2x+1$

12 $(ax+b)\times 2ax+a\times(ax^2+b);\ a(3ax^2+2bx+b)$

13 $\dfrac{(1+x)\times 0-2\times 1}{(1+x)^2};\ \dfrac{-2}{(1+x)^2}$

14 $\dfrac{(1-2x^2)\times 0-3\times(-4x)}{(1-2x^2)^2};\ \dfrac{12x}{(1-2x^2)^2}$

15 $\dfrac{(x-1)\times 1-x\times 1}{(x-1)^2};\ \dfrac{-1}{(x-1)^2}$

16 $\dfrac{\left(x^2+1\right)\times1-x\times2x}{\left(x^2+1\right)^2}$; $\dfrac{1-x^2}{\left(x^2+1\right)^2}$

17 $\dfrac{(4-x)\times1-(4+x)\times(-1)}{(4-x)^2}$; $\dfrac{8}{(x-4)^2}$

18 $\dfrac{(5-x)\times5-(1+5x)\times(-1)}{(5-x)^2}$; $\dfrac{26}{(x-5)^2}$

19 $\dfrac{\left(1+x^2\right)\times(-2x)-\left(1-x^2\right)\times2x}{\left(1+x^2\right)^2}$; $\dfrac{-4x}{\left(x^2+1\right)^2}$

20 $\dfrac{\left(1-x^2\right)\times2x-\left(1+x^2\right)\times(-2x)}{\left(1-x^2\right)^2}$; $\dfrac{4x}{\left(1-x^2\right)^2}$

21 $\dfrac{(1+2x)^2\times1-x\times2(1+2x)\times2}{(1+2x)^4}$; $\dfrac{1-2x}{(1+2x)^3}$

22 $\dfrac{(x+2)^2\times2-(2x+1)\times2(x+2)}{(x+2)^4}$; $\dfrac{-2x+2}{(x+2)^3}$

23 $\dfrac{(3x+2)^3\times1-x\times3(3x+2)^2\times3}{(3x+2)^6}$; $\dfrac{-6x+2}{(3x+2)^4}$

24 $\dfrac{(x+3)^4\times1-x\times4(x+3)^3\times1}{(x+3)^8}$; $\dfrac{3-3x}{(x+3)^5}$

25 $\dfrac{(x+1)\times\frac{1}{2}\left(x^2+1\right)^{-\frac{1}{2}}\times2x-\left(x^2+1\right)^{\frac{1}{2}}\times1}{(x+1)^2}$; $\dfrac{x-1}{(x+1)^2\left(x^2+1\right)^{\frac{1}{2}}}$

26 $\dfrac{\left(x^2+1\right)^{\frac{1}{2}}\times2-(2x+1)\times\frac{1}{2}\left(x^2+1\right)^{-\frac{1}{2}}\times2x}{\left(x^2+1\right)}$; $\dfrac{2-x}{\left(x^2+1\right)^{\frac{3}{2}}}$

Exercise 13, page 74

1 $-4\sin x$ **2** $5\cos5x$

3 $\frac{1}{2}\cos\frac{1}{2}x$ **4** $2\sec^2 2x$

5 $-6\sin3x+9\cos3x$ **6** $-\sin\frac{1}{2}x-\frac{1}{2}\cos\frac{1}{2}x$

7 $2\cos(2x+\pi)$ **8** $\frac{1}{2}\sin\frac{1}{2}(\pi-x)$

9 $4\sin x\cos x$ **10** $-10\cos5x\sin5x$

11 $\frac{3}{2}\sin^2\frac{1}{2}x\cos\frac{1}{2}x$

12 $6\tan 3x\sec^2 3x$

13 $\cos 2x - 2x\sin 2x$

14 $2x\tan\frac{1}{2}x + \frac{1}{2}x^2\sec^2\frac{1}{2}x$

15 $\sin^2 x + 2x\sin x\cos x$

16 $x\cos x$

17 $\dfrac{x\cos x - \sin x}{x^2}$

18 $\dfrac{2\sin 2x}{(1+\cos 2x)^2}$

19 $\dfrac{-\cos x}{\sin^2 x}$

20 $\dfrac{-2\cos x - x\sin x}{2x^2\sqrt{\cos x}}$

21 Maximum of $\sqrt{2}$ when $x = \frac{3}{4}\pi$; minimum of $-\sqrt{2}$ when $x = \frac{7}{4}\pi$.

22 $4y = 4x + \pi - 4$; $4y = -4x - \pi - 4$

23 $\left(0, \dfrac{4}{\pi}\right)$

24 $\left(-\dfrac{5\pi}{12}, -\dfrac{\sqrt{3}}{2}\right)$, $\left(-\dfrac{\pi}{12}, \dfrac{\sqrt{3}}{2}\right)$, $\left(\dfrac{7\pi}{12}, -\dfrac{\sqrt{3}}{2}\right)$, $\left(\dfrac{11\pi}{12}, \dfrac{\sqrt{3}}{2}\right)$

25 $50\cos 5 = 14.183\ldots$ cm s^{-1}, $-250\sin 5 = 239.7\ldots$ cm s^{-2}, 10 cm

26 $\frac{5}{6}\pi = 2.618\ldots$ m s^{-1}, 9 hours

Exercise 14, page 82

1 $4e^{4x}$

2 $e^{\frac{1}{4}x}$

3 $4xe^{2x^2}$

4 $-6e^{-2x}$

5 $-e^{3-x}$

6 $e^{-\frac{1}{2}x}$

7 $\dfrac{1}{x}$

8 $\dfrac{2}{x}$

9 $\dfrac{2}{2x+3}$

10 $\dfrac{2x+2}{x^2+2x}$

11 1

12 1

13 $-\tan x$

14 $\dfrac{2}{x}$

15 $\dfrac{2px+q}{px^2+qx+r}$

16 $\dfrac{1}{2x}$

17 $(2x - x^2)e^{-x}$

18 $\ln x$

19 $\dfrac{4}{4-x^2}$

20 $\dfrac{2ab}{b^2x^2-a^2}$

21 At $\left(\frac{1}{2}\ln 2, \frac{1}{2}\right)$

22 Maximum of $\dfrac{1}{e}$ when $x = 1$

23 Maximum of $\dfrac{1}{\sqrt{2}e^{\frac{1}{4}\pi}}$ when $x = \frac{1}{4}\pi$, $e^{-2\pi}$.

24 $10\ln 10 = 23.03\ldots$ min, $0.6\,^\circ C\,\text{min}^{-1}$

25 $\dfrac{1}{k}\ln 2$, $2kA$

26 $x = \pm\frac{1}{2}\sqrt{2}$

27 $x = \pm\sigma$

Exercise 15, page 86

1 $\quad 1 + \dfrac{dy}{dx}$

2 $\quad 2 - \dfrac{dy}{dx}$

3 $\quad 4x - 3\dfrac{dy}{dx}$

4 $\quad 2y\dfrac{dy}{dx}$

5 $\quad 2xy\dfrac{dy}{dx} + y^2$

6 $\quad 2x^2y\dfrac{dy}{dx} + 2xy^2$

7 $\quad \dfrac{x\dfrac{dy}{dx} - y}{x^2}$ or $\dfrac{1}{x}\dfrac{dy}{dx} - \dfrac{y}{x^2}$

8 $\quad \dfrac{y - x\dfrac{dy}{dx}}{y^2}$ or $\dfrac{1}{y} - \dfrac{x}{y^2}\dfrac{dy}{dx}$

9 $\quad \cos y\dfrac{dy}{dx}$

10 $\quad \dfrac{1}{x} + \dfrac{1}{y}\dfrac{dy}{dx}$

11 $\quad e^y\dfrac{dy}{dx}$

12 $\quad 2ye^{y^2}\dfrac{dy}{dx}$

13 $\quad -\dfrac{x+y}{x+2y}$

14 $\quad -\dfrac{5x^4 + 2y^2}{5y^4 + 4xy}$

15 $\quad \dfrac{2y}{y+1}$

16 $\quad -\dfrac{2x + y^2}{2y + 2xy}$

17 $\quad -\frac{8}{9}$

18 $\quad -\frac{1}{3}$

19 $\quad -\frac{1}{2}$

20 $\quad -4$

Exercise 16, page 89

1 $\quad -2$

2 $\quad -\frac{1}{5}$

3 $\quad \dfrac{2t+1}{2t-1}$

4 $\quad \dfrac{-t}{t+1}$

5 $-2te^{-t}$

6 $\dfrac{e^{t}+e^{-t}}{e^{t}-e^{-t}}$

7 -1

8 $-\tan t$

9 $\dfrac{2t-t^{4}}{1-2t^{3}}$

10 1

11 $-\frac{2}{3}$

12 $-\frac{1}{3}$

13 $\frac{1}{2}$

14 $-\frac{1}{2}$

15 e^{-4}

16 $6e^{2}$

17 $4y=x+4$

18 $9y+x=-6$

19 $y=-x$

20 $4y+2x=-3\sqrt{3}$

Exercise 17, page 93

1 $32\pi\,\mathrm{cm^{2}\,s^{-1}}$

2 $6\pi\,\mathrm{cm\,s^{-1}}$

3 $16\pi\,\mathrm{cm^{2}\,s^{-1}}$

4 $216\,\mathrm{cm^{3}\,s^{-1}};144\,\mathrm{cm^{2}\,s^{-1}}$

5 $\dfrac{5}{2\pi}\,\mathrm{cm\,s^{-1}}$

6 $\dfrac{5}{\pi}\,\mathrm{cm\,s^{-1}}$

7 $\frac{4}{15}\,\mathrm{cm\,s^{-1}}$

8 $\frac{8}{5}\,\mathrm{cm\,s^{-1}}$

9 $30\,\mathrm{cm^{3}\,s^{-1}}$

10 $16\pi\,\mathrm{cm^{2}\,s^{-1}}$

Exercise 18, page 97

1 0.3

2 -0.05

3 0

4 $-0.0453\ldots$

5 2.94

6 1.005

7 0.4975

8 0.495

9 5.1

10 $4.0208\ldots$

11 0.0416

12 9800

Exercise 19, page 105

1

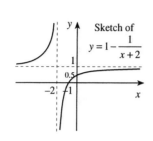

Sketch of
$$y = 1 - \frac{1}{x+2}$$

2

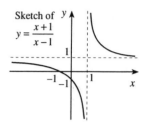

Sketch of
$$y = \frac{x+1}{x-1}$$

3

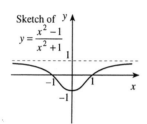

Sketch of
$$y = \frac{x^2 - 1}{x^2 + 1}$$

4

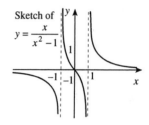

Sketch of
$$y = \frac{x}{x^2 - 1}$$

5

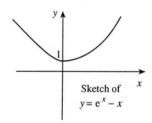

$(2, 4e^{-2})$

Sketch of
$$y = x^2 e^{-x}$$

6

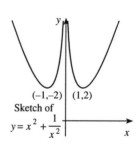

Sketch of
$$y = e^x - x$$

7

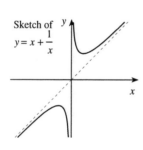

Sketch of
$$y = x + \frac{1}{x}$$

8

$(-1, -2)$ $(1, 2)$

Sketch of
$$y = x^2 + \frac{1}{x^2}$$

9

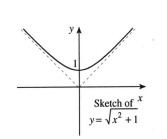

Sketch of
$y = \sqrt{x^2 + 1}$

10

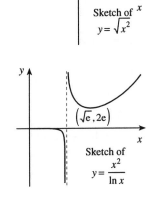

Sketch of
$y = \sqrt{x^2}$

11

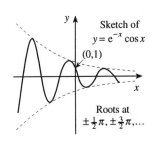

Sketch of
$y = x - \ln x$

$(1,1)$

12

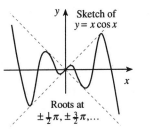

$\left(\sqrt{e}, 2e\right)$

Sketch of
$y = \dfrac{x^2}{\ln x}$

13

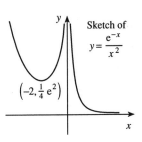

Sketch of
$y = e^{-x} \cos x$

$(0,1)$

Roots at
$\pm \tfrac{1}{2}\pi, \pm \tfrac{3}{2}\pi, \ldots$

14

Sketch of
$y = x \cos x$

Roots at
$\pm \tfrac{1}{2}\pi, \pm \tfrac{3}{2}\pi, \ldots$

15

Sketch of
$y = \dfrac{e^{-x}}{x^2}$

$\left(-2, \tfrac{1}{4}e^2\right)$

16

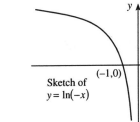

$(-1,0)$

Sketch of
$y = \ln(-x)$

Revision exercise 1, page 106

1 $\dfrac{1}{\sqrt{x}}$, $\tfrac{1}{2}$

2 $x + 6y = 57$, $3\tfrac{1}{6}$

3 $3\cos 2 = -1.248...$m s^{-1}, $-3\sin 2 = -2.728...$m s^{-2}

4 Maximum at $(-2,28)$, minimum at $(4,-80)$, point of inflexion at $(1,-26)$

5 $\dfrac{x-1}{(x+1)^2\left(x^2+1\right)^{\frac{1}{2}}}$

6 Quadratic, Type A, $(0,-3)$, $(-1,0)$, $(3,0)$, minimum at $(1,-4)$

Revision exercise 2, page 106

1 $-\frac{1}{54}$

2 $4x+y=1$

3 A_0, $\frac{1}{2}kA_0$

4 18 cm wide by 12 cm high

5 1

6 $2x\sin\left(x^2+1\right)+2x^3\cos\left(x^2+1\right)$

Revision exercise 3, page 107

1 $\left(\frac{1}{2},\frac{2}{5}\right),\left(-\frac{1}{2},-\frac{2}{5}\right)$

2 $\sqrt{2}$ cm min^{-1}

3 The points $(n\pi,0)$, for any integer n, are points of inflexion

4 5 m s^{-1} or -5 m s^{-1}

5 Minimum at $(0,0)$, maximum at $\left(2,4e^{-2}\right)$

6 Cubic, Type D, $(0,3)$, minimum at $(-3,-15)$, maximum at $\left(\frac{1}{3},3\frac{14}{27}\right)$

Revision exercise 4, page 107

1 $\dfrac{y}{3y-2x}$

2 $y=x-3$

3 Minimum at $(0,1)$; no points of inflexion

4 $13\sqrt{13}$

5 0.16π m^3

6 $x=2.272...$, $y=3.464...$

Revision exercise 5, page 107

1

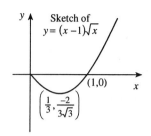

2 $\frac{5}{6}\pi \approx 2.62$ rad

3 $2x + 4x \ln x$

4 4 and –4.

5 $\dfrac{\mathrm{d}y}{\mathrm{d}x} = -\dfrac{\sqrt{y}}{\sqrt{x}}$

6 $a^2 > 3b$

Revision exercise 6, page 108

1 $16\frac{2}{3}$ cm^2 s^{-1}

2 $\dfrac{2x-1}{x^{\frac{3}{2}}}$

3 Minima at $(1,0)$ and $(-1,0)$; maximum at $(0,1)$

4 $\dfrac{\mathrm{d}y}{\mathrm{d}x} = \dfrac{4x-3y}{3x-8y}$

5 $4x - 2y = \sqrt{2}$

6 $\frac{1}{2}\sqrt{2}$ and $-\frac{1}{2}\sqrt{2}$

Index